one town's son

a journey home to find the truth

Kevin Troxall

One Town's Son was composed from tape-recorded interviews, personal observation, diary entries, and official public records. The author's personal memories have also been used to further the story without diminishing factual evidence. Unrecorded reconstructive conversations were derived from the recollection of the author. Certain names have been changed.

Introduction

A few miles before entering the state park, visitors are greeted with various signs declaring adultery a sin, abortion an abomination, and a man that chooses to lie with another man a sinner. Jesus, as they proclaim, is this country's only hope of survival.

These homemade billboards are not easily overlooked. Each massive structure seems to block out the sunlight, casting a shadow across the grassy terrain onto the pavement of the winding road. For a split second, day turns dark as travelers cruise past the scripture-laden signs, and if not previously noticed, one's eye quickly catches the ominous advertisement of the gospel. Here, along this stretch of the Bible Belt, Jesus loves you--so long as you're the same as everyone else.

These fearsome warnings seem entirely out of place against the backdrop of such serene beauty. The farther you travel into this country the more pastoral the landscape becomes. Green fields grow greener, local fauna is noticeably more present, and the afternoon air, while it can, at times, be thick, seems to dissolve slowly into crystal clear purity, as though it is lighter than nature intended.

It is May in southern Kentucky. By now every tree has flourished, every flower has blossomed and the entire landscape has taken on its richest hues. Without a tall building in sight, the scene is almost surreal. One would think only artists could capture an environment so vividly. But not today. Today the sky is blue. Not azure, not aqua, nor teal, nor indigo. It is simply blue, just as the hills are green. In their purest shades, the land and the sky are perfect.

Each blade of native bluegrass is flawless and seems to grow symmetrically along the earth. The hills slope evenly throughout this picturesque scene as if created by basic mathematical equations. Even the cows that dot the land, here and there, have precise markings on their hides, prompting observers to wonder if they've been cloned.

Perfecting the view, stand uneven, wooden fences along the roadside. Like a movie set, these props seem to have been constructed precisely this way in order to capture a feel for the location. These and the small rural bait shops that tend to multiply closer to the entrance of the park are the few man-made features along this final stretch of road. Each of these depots looks exactly as one would expect them to in this idealized landscape.

Common to what the locals refer to as "these parts" sits a single room structure with a pitched roof, covered in cracked asphalt shingles. A metal screen door rests on rusty hinges. No other door is present. Beside it hangs a notice board that reads, "LIVE BAIT!" In the gravel yard are various accoutrements with a nautical theme. Items such as a canoe, buoys, oars, and large rope litter the ground. Inside the canoe is a giant fish, made from a scrap of plywood and colorfully painted to look like a largemouth bass--one of the many species common to this region.

Up on the porch, to the right of the screen door, are two rocking chairs; obviously handcrafted and not identical. One has arms, the other does not. The slats used on each seat run in opposite directions, and the one closest to the front door shows signs of considerably more wear. To the left of the door is a vending machine. Outsiders might see this as a novel reproduction, but in fact, it is original. This large, red metal box with its thin glass door and tarnished handle still dispenses soda in dusty, green glass bottles for twenty-five cents.

The store's interior resembles grandma's attic, filled with keepsakes, reminders, and souvenirs. The walls are covered with local newspaper clippings, photographs of fishermen posing with their prize-winning catches, and various fliers for hunting events, boat sales, and announcements for local fishing competitions – most of which are yellowed and years overdue. Completing the decorations on the walls are numerous, stuffed fish mounted on wooden plaques. Species such as crappie, bass, catfish, and bluegill (all native here) adorn the walls. Then there are some, such as barracuda and marlin, that one can't help but wonder from where they came.

Fishing rods in an assortment of sizes lean against the back wall. A display of reels rests under glass beside the cash register. From fasteners in the ceiling are various nets and creels. Styrofoam coolers are sold individually, although some contain other fishing needs such as hooks, lures, spools of fly line and insect repellant.

At the front of one long table are tackle boxes filled with artificial baits including rooster tails, sassy shad and buck tail jigs. But the main supply of income for this shop, the reason so many visitors frequent this place, is at the far end of the table. There, with the sense of life present, are small, clear, plastic tubs with tiny holes on top. Some of these containers are filled with dirt that hold night crawlers and earthworms. Others house crawfish and minnows. Still others simply contain bits of liver or chicken guts to entice unsuspecting fish.

Back on the road, just a few yards south, is the entrance to Barren River Lake State Park Resort. A narrow road leads cars down a clearing of the grounds passing horse stables and hiking trails before finding its way to the front door of the Louie B. Nunn Lodge. Named after a native of the county and a former Republican governor of the Commonwealth, the Lodge overlooks a 10,000-acre lake in Lucas, Kentucky.

The lake is a favorite of local families looking for fun and relaxation, as well as a place to entertain during the summer months. Many notable area names keep their collection of houseboats, pontoons, and jet skis on hand at the lake's docks for such occasions. But the water isn't just for them. Every year thousands of visitors flock to the area and partake of the lake's beauty. Its pristine surface shines like a mirror in the afternoon sun while underneath its temperatures remain cool and soothing.

The Lodge itself houses 51 guest suites, three conference rooms, and two private dining halls featuring some of the area's finest cuisine and friendly service. With wood paneling on the walls, exposed wood beams, and an abundance of natural light through two large walls of windows, the Lodge seems better suited for a Rocky Mountain getaway than the rolling hills of Kentucky.

In addition to the Lodge, the Park also accommodates 22 cottages on its campgrounds, used privately as well as for public functions. The cabins include all the modern amenities one would need as well as some of the most spectacular views of the lake and surrounding countryside. Their seclusion, nestled in the woods, offers a charming and cozy excuse to relax and get away from it all. For larger groups, they present another location in which to meet.

Over the past several years many graduating classes from the local high schools in Barren County have used the Lodge and its facilities for themselves. On the evening of May 29th, the Glasgow High class of 1994 met for its tenth-year reunion. At 7:00 p.m. a dinner was served for those in attendance. The evening was just beginning.

At 7:30 p.m. Scotty Martin arrived at the Lodge. Amy Claywell, a family friend, had driven him there from his home in Bowling Green, about a half hour away. Scotty didn't own a car at the time and had called her for transportation. On the drive to the reunion Scotty seemed excited about the evening, mentioning to Amy some of the people he hoped to see. Stepping out of the car he thanked her for the ride and joined his cousin, Michelle, who was already waiting for him at the entrance to the Lodge. The two made their way inside.

By 8:00 p.m. the majority of classmates had all arrived and a hired band played music for the next four hours. Many of those in attendance, mostly females, danced to the live band.

At various tables throughout the room people were chatting and reminiscing. As in high school each table contained its own cliques, catching up on old times. Taylor Bale Kuczynski, class president and organizer of the reunion, got up to speak and welcomed everyone to the occasion. At midnight the scheduled party ended. Many had come and gone, but for those who chose to continue the revelry, cabins had been rented for the evening.

Cabin 507 is one of the cottages closest to the Lodge itself. About 400 feet south, it sits downhill behind the rear of the Lodge. From this part of the building there is only one exit; through the Lodge's kitchen. For the employees who smoke, this area is for them. To the left of the kitchen is a concrete ramp with a steep decline that serves as the loading area for the building. On either side of the ramp are concrete walls measuring eleven-feet at their tallest reach. Two concrete wheel stops are affixed at the bottom of the slope to prevent loading trucks from backing into the entryway. To get from this spot to the front entrance of the Lodge one would have to walk up the 80-foot incline and circle his way another 200 yards through a small employee parking lot to the front door. Two light fixtures are installed on either side of the retaining walls, but on this night, the bulbs are shot, and the area is especially dark.

After the reunion was over, John Dickenson and his wife invited several people back to Cabin 507. About thirty people arrived, including Bryant Vincent and his wife Holli, Stacey and Andrew McChord, Chris York, and Blake Oliver, all whom had scheduled to stay the night in 507. Though two other cabins had been previously rented for the evening it was here that most initially congregated.

The after-party continued in the cabin until the early hours of the next day. Many provided their own alcohol and shared with those who hadn't. They drank, listened to music, and talked on the front porch of the cottage. Scotty Martin was having a beer on the porch when Stacy Phillips showed up. Earlier at the Lodge they had discussed how they were going to get home afterwards. Stacy's ride had already left and Scotty told her he didn't have a way back either. Since both lived in Bowling Green they decided to stay a while longer and split a cab if necessary.

Scotty and Stacy had been in the band together during high school. In fact, most of the people Scotty seemed to be hanging out with during the reunion were former band members, so it was a surprise for Stacy to see Scotty having a drink on the porch with Blake Oliver and Chris York, guys Stacy would later refer to as "the jock types." But for now everything seemed fine. Everyone seemed to be getting along well.

Scotty had been living in Bowling Green for a couple of years. Prior to that he resided in Lexington where he had attended the University of Kentucky. It was here that Scotty felt more comfortable being himself. He could be openly gay and not worry about how to act or what to say. In Bowling Green, however, things were a bit more reserved and he was more cautious of his behavior. According to his sister, Brandi, Scotty was a very private person, even when he lived in Lexington. He rarely discussed dates and would never offer up information unless someone else inquired first. He was quiet, respectful. He had a great love for his family, which is why he decided to move closer to them, leaving Lexington.

Upon his move to Bowling Green he started shopping at the local mall which is where he would frequently run into old classmates – classmates he had missed since graduating high school. A week before the reunion while Stacy was visiting him for dinner, Scotty had remarked that he was excited to see his old friends, Blake Haines and Ann Gentry. He never mentioned whether he was afraid of seeing anyone at the reunion.

Excusing herself to the bathroom, Stacy left the porch of the cabin and headed inside. Before she could finish someone knocked on the door.

"It's me. I'm coming in," Scotty said. Stacy told him to wait a minute, and he did.

Upon opening the door, Scotty asked, "Do you want to do something?" And with that, Scotty pulled out a vile from his bag and asked if she wanted some.

"No thanks," Stacy replied.

Scotty then snorted the unknown substance while Stacy left him alone in the bathroom.

At 1:30 in the morning, Stacy obtained a ride with a friend back to her parents' home in Glasgow. Before leaving, she asked Scotty if he was ready to go, but he had decided to stay the night instead. She then offered him a ride in the morning if he wanted to call her when he woke up. That was the last time Stacy would see him alive.

Later in the night the crowd started to thin out as Scotty's classmates either headed home or to their respective cabins. Around 3:00 a.m. only a handful of guests were still talking outside Cabin 507. Angelo Pedicini had joined Blake Oliver, John Dickenson and Bryant Vincent on the porch. Scotty was there too; all of them messing around with a skunk a short distance from the cottage.

Blake stood up and headed inside. The guys figured he had had enough and was going to bed. Angelo glanced over and noticed Scotty trailing in behind Blake. He didn't put much thought into it until five minutes later when Scotty came barreling out the cabin door past the others and up the hill towards the Lodge without saying a word.

A few seconds later, Blake emerged once again and told the guys remaining on the porch that Scotty had just made a pass at him.

"He just offered me a blowjob," Blake laughed.

Angelo was shocked. The others howled in disbelief.

"Yeah, right!" Bryant exclaimed.

"I'm serious," Blake said. "I'm serious!"

For a while the others harassed Blake about his story then shrugged it off as no big deal. Several minutes later they saw Scotty returning from the hill towards the cabin. Again, he said nothing and headed indoors. The others continued to socialize a while longer. Angelo grew tired and eventually departed to his own bed in Cabin 504.

Around 7:00 a.m. the following morning Taylor and her husband were awakened in their own cabin by a phone call from the front desk of the Lodge. The person on the other end told her that there had been an accident and she needed to come to the rear of the loading dock as soon as possible. Immediately she and David got dressed and headed outside.

When they arrived at the scene they saw a body lying at the bottom of the dock. The head was resting in a pool of blood beside one of the concrete wheel stops. When Taylor walked further down the slope she confirmed it was Scotty. He was unconscious, barely breathing. She grabbed her husband tightly. "This is all my fault," she sobbed.

Several Parks' officials were already at the rear of the Lodge, including Ranger Veachell Adwell. He had been called to the scene by the front desk clerk who, in turn, had heard from one of the cooks in the kitchen that a body had been found out back.

Taylor and David took off towards the cabins to inform the other reunion-goers what had happened. About that time is when emergency services personnel, including a Stat-Care helicopter, arrived. They began to treat Scotty's injuries immediately, transporting him to Vanderbilt Medical Hospital in Nashville. He would remain in a coma for ten days before passing away on June 10th.

David knocked on the door of Cabin 504 when Mark Nelson opened it. He explained to Mark that Scotty had been seriously hurt in an accident. Apparently he had fallen off the loading dock and was badly injured. Rangers were trying to contact Scotty's parents.

After getting dressed, Mark and several others headed off to the Lodge where they discussed what had happened over breakfast. Later, on their way back to the cabin, they stopped at the loading dock where they observed rangers taping off the area. Mark spoke to Rangers Adwell and Hogue that morning, describing the events of the previous evening. After his conversation with them, he and Angelo saw Chris York in the parking lot tying down a motorcycle to the bed of his truck.

"Rangers are probably gonna come down to the cabin so you better get those beer cans cleaned up," Mark told Chris.

Chris looked confused. "Why are the rangers comin' down here?"

"About Scotty," was all Mark said.

Chris shot back, "Man, the hell with Scotty. He came on to Blake and Bryant last night."

Mark froze. This was the first he was hearing about any sexual advances towards the guys. He then went on to explain to Chris that Scotty had been found in his own blood at the bottom of the loading dock. Chris seemed surprised.

Leaving him in the parking lot, Mark and Angelo headed towards Cabin 507 where they told the same story to those remaining. Neither Blake, nor Bryant was there. They had long since left the Park before anyone else had woken.

One

"I'm going to fucking kill you if you don't shut the hell up!" Even with headphones on and my music blaring in my ears I could clearly make out the yelling match at the far end of the train car. Elbow to elbow I stood, trying not to waiver as my one, free hand barely grasped a steel pole high above a very pregnant woman's head. All notion of personal space was forgotten as the packed train jostled passengers to and fro, bumping against one another. A tall, slender man in need of a serious haircut continued to unknowingly jab me in the shoulder with his backpack, twice his size and containing God knows what.

"Get outta my fuckin' face!" screamed a second man's voice.

Above ground it was another typical Chicago winter, but here in the train car, well below the earth's surface, with the heat cranked up and multiple bodies radiating underneath layers of warm clothing it felt like summer in Death Valley.

Not expecting the dry, balmy conditions I was currently experiencing, my outfit consisted of little more than six layers of clothing topped off with a new Burberry messenger bag I was trying to protect from others' sweaty fingers. At this point, however, I, myself, was sweating all over my designer duds and dreaming of stripping down to nothing.

"Nobody wants to hear your goddamn conversation!" It was the first man's voice again. The fight was apparently another cellphone dispute. Most people have no sense of their own voice when talking on a cellphone and few people on the CTA have the patience for those who talk louder than necessary. In fact, this was the second such fight I had experienced during the day. My morning commute on the bus contained two junior high school kids who seemed to be competing with each other for Loudest Brat. Eventually the driver pulled over and yelled at both kids to get off her bus. Reluctantly, they continued their phone conversations and hopped out the back door; not before each gave the driver the finger and screamed profanities. Half the passengers clapped when the bus started moving again.

Back on the train I was still getting poked by the backpack filled with items I was imagining could be inside: camping equipment? power tools? a severed head? We neared North and Clybourn, the last stop on the Red Line before riding the elevated tracks above ground. From the fractured view I had of the outside, I could see rows of people waiting for the train to arrive, not knowing how any of them could possibly fit their way onto my car.

The conductor presented himself over the intercom by announcing, "Please allow passengers off the train. This train is full but we do have another Red Line immediately following this one. Again, please allow passengers off of the train and we do have another train right behind this one." When the doors opened, no one moved. Everyone looked around to see if anyone was approaching to exit, but no one did. And though one small girl fought to join our car, her efforts were futile. A bell chimed and the doors closed once again leaving her on the platform to attempt entry on the train that followed.

As our train took off again, gravity intervened and forced the standing passengers backwards. This time my body fell at the man's backpack, still containing the severed head I was convinced was inside. Two young businessmen, who had previously been behind my left side, were now both stepping on my feet due in part to the quick take off of the train. One of the men tried retaining his balance only to fall against the other, in turn causing me to lose my valuable grip of the steel bar. Quickly trying to regain my hold, the pregnant woman's face came within inches of my armpit.

"Excuse me!" she lashed out in a tone of disgust.

"I'm so sorry," I said. Realizing that I had lost my bar, I now relied on the backpack for support, casually leaning on its dullest edge.

"When are you gonna get off this fuckin' train?" The first man was back to yelling again.

"Fuck you!" was the second man's simple reply.

In a playlist of over 2,000, the one song that I despised the most had just begun to play on my iPod. Unless I expected to lose my balance and either fall down completely or into the arms of a pregnant woman who already despised me or the grip of a serial killer with a severed head attached to his back, I knew I had to endure "The Sound of the Atom Splitting" for the next four minutes. There was no way at this moment I could reach into my messenger bag and advance to one of the dozens of more enjoyable Pet Shop Boys' songs.

The train continued to speed along the track while its passengers, resembling canned sardines, gave in to its aggressive beatings, its heat, and its confines. Suddenly, the train came to an abrupt stop. The same two businessmen landed once again on my feet while I managed to get pinned between an unborn child and a decapitated head. Once everyone had gained their composure, there was silence, except for the two men still at the far end with their verbal assaults and the awful song I was now able to change to a more favorable one due to our grinding halt.

Although I have a fairly strong case of claustrophobia, I am generally not panic-stricken in the subway so long as the train is in constant motion. I was now no longer moving, packed in an overcrowded car with layers of unnecessary clothing on within seconds of freaking out. I tried to focus on the music playing in my ears while not paying particular attention to the lyrics. It was Alanis Morissette singing, ironically, "Ironic."

It was a minute and a half before the conductor announced, "Workers are clearing an item from the track." During those seconds, which felt to me like hours, my breathing was becoming hurried. I closed my eyes and tried to pretend I was simply listening to my music instead of showing any signs of distress. My mind began to fight itself, competing for thoughts between the dozens of things I had to do before leaving town the following day and the list of ways I didn't wish to die, most notably on a packed train car buried underground. Then I thought of Scotty.

"Ladies and gentlemen," the conductor began, "we'll be moving shortly." No sooner had the voice made its prediction than the train started slowly accelerating again. My breathing began to stabilize. We picked up speed. My fears lessened. Within seconds we were finally ascending into the open night. My head was clearer and I was relieved. I could see buildings and trees. I knew at some point I would be getting off this ride and would possibly kiss the ground.

When we arrived at Fullerton, enough people were getting off that it caused the entire load of passengers to readjust their positions. Several seats became available. Like vultures circling their prey, a disgruntled mob of standing riders eyed those open seats and moved in on the attack once they were free. My pregnant cohort was able to obtain a seat herself, not before forcing her way through the crowd, stomach thrust forward, and demanding, "Can a pregnant lady PLEASE sit down?!" At least she was out of my way. Now I was able to acquire a bit more support on the metal pole. But just as soon as a third of the train car emptied, another two-thirds tried to maneuver themselves on board. I was not about to give up my section of pole. I grabbed it tightly as the masses descended, not letting go.

When the doors shut again I heard a familiar voice through the music in my headphones. I turned my head to the right to find that I was now sharing space with the cellphone guy, still in the middle of a conversation.

"Yeah, I know. He's such an asshole," he said. "I hate that fucker."

During the shuffling of passengers at Fullerton he must have managed to work his way to the other end of the train car and was now carrying on with no regard to us around him.

"If I see that asshole again, I'm gonna fuckin' kill his ass," he continued.

Though I was able to turn up my iPod slightly, it was not enough to drown out Mr. Cellphone completely. I could also begin to tell by the eyes of those standing next to me that the music pouring through my headphones was now just as annoying to them as his talking was. But at this point, I didn't care. I had six more stops to go before getting off the train and I wasn't about to spend it listening to this jerk spout obscenities.

I looked at the time. 6:55 p.m. I should have been home by now. I hate being late, especially when I have a million things to do. Outside the train I could barely make out the beginnings of a slight flurry of snow gently falling. As we approached Belmont we had to once again stop, this time allowing the Brown Line train to pass and make its way ahead of us. The restructuring of the Belmont station for the past year had been a nuisance for all riders of the CTA. In order to improve the station and tracks, the Red, Brown, and Purple line trains were all sharing one track into Belmont. This was adding a lot more time to my lateness than I was hoping.

As we stood aside, waiting for the adjacent train to proceed, I could feel a slight vibration in my outer coat pocket. My own cellphone was ringing, but witnessing the rage expressed by those around me, I dared not answer it. Mr. Cellphone snapped again, "Get the fuck outta here! What? Okay, bye." And with that, his conversation was finally over. Now the only noise permeating our end of the train car was the fierce sounds of my pumped up music, blaring to overcompensate for Mr. Cellphone's voice. Suddenly, I was the jerk.

I reached inside the side pocket of my messenger bag in an attempt to lessen the volume. The train started to move again so I quickly grabbed the sacred metal pole I had come to claim as my own. Until the next stop I would continue to annoy everyone in my vicinity with my rhythmic din.

On the approach into Belmont, most people who were sitting stood up to exit the car. Another group of vultures got into place. This time, when the doors opened, a ferocious game of musical chairs ensued. I had decided not to take part in this round and hang on once again to my favorite piece of steel. As passengers began to leave the car and cold, gusty sheets of wind entered the train I was beginning to once again be thankful for the amount of garments I was wearing.

Before the doors closed at Belmont I was able to turn the volume back down on my iPod and advance towards a more peaceful song I thought would make my ride more enjoyable. While searching for said song I overheard the shrill sound of barking dogs, obviously coming from nearby. I knew that since animals were not permitted on public transportation this had to be someone's cellphone ring. Surprising no one, Mr. Cellphone answered the call.

"What the fuck do you want, man?" he laughed.

I began to wonder how I ended up on the train ride from hell. I had a list of chores I had to finish before the night was over, I had clothes to pack, and I had a small mountain of paperwork to review and questions to write before I was to leave town. It was then I remembered the old joke of how to get God to laugh: make a plan.

I could see the glowing Cubs sign at Wrigley Field when we approached the Addison station. Had it been two years ago I would be exiting the train now, but Kory and I moved out of the neighborhood in order to buy a place, so I still had five more stops to go.

With each stop, fewer people entered the car and more were getting off. At the Wilson stop, Mr. Cellphone stood up. I was certain I was about to be free of him until he reached into his pants pocket, pulled out a Blackberry and sat back down. "Yeah hang on, lemme check," he told the person on the other end of the phone. I think this was the first time he had said one thing that wasn't obscene. "No, that won't work," he continued, "I gotta fuckin' bar mitzvah I gotta go to."

At Lawrence I decided to finally sit down. There had been a few empty seats since Addison, but I had grown accustomed to the pole. Sitting next to a woman, carefully trying to solve a Sudoku, I decided to check the voicemail from my earlier call. It was Brandi, Scotty's sister. "Hey Kevin, I was just calling to let you know that we're all set for Sunday at 3:00 p.m. Call my cell if anything changes before then. Otherwise, I'll see you then. Okay? Bye."

Sunday was just two days away, but it felt like a lifetime. I started getting nervous. Am I prepared enough, I thought to myself? I couldn't believe this was finally happening. I kept wondering how Brandi was going to react. Would she answer all my questions or would there be anything off limits?

"Excuse me," said the woman sitting next to me.

"I'm sorry," I asked, turning down my music again to hear what she was saying.

"This is my stop," she explained.

I looked up to see where we were. Argyle. "Oh right, sure." I picked up my bag, stood and stepped aside so she could exit. Berwyn was next. Finally my stop. I sat back down and put my phone inside my pocket. I advanced another song and waited a few more seconds before I decided to stand and lean against the door. Pulling into Berwyn, I turned back to see Mr. Cellphone still chatting away. "Yeah, fuck that," was the last thing I heard him say.

As I stepped onto the platform at the station snow was still quietly drifting, barely covering the ground below. Not wanting to slip, I held onto the railing as I descended the stairs to the street level. At the bottom, passing through the turnstile, I once again felt my pocket vibrate. This time, however, it was a text message. I reached for my phone as I stepped outside into the frosty air. The number 92 bus was idling, waiting to pick up transfers from the Red Line on the sidewalk. I placed my phone back in my pocket in exchange for my wallet. After paying the bus fare and finding a seat in the rear, I opened the text. "Where r u?" it said. It was from Kory. In response I wrote, "On bus. B home soon. C U later 2nite." I noticed then that both my phone and iPod were in need of recharging. I was hoping my music would at least last another twenty minutes until I got home.

Looking around, I saw a greater-than-normal amount of litter on the floor of the bus. A *Chicago Tribune* had exploded, it appeared, and been trampled on by every passengers' wet snowshoes. As the bus took off, a half-empty, plastic soda bottle rolled aimlessly back and forth among our feet. No one picked it up.

As we turned onto Broadway from Berwyn I noticed a hole developing in one of my gloves. I took it off to examine it closer. A rip in the "V" between the ring finger and pinky was beginning to expose my hand. It appeared as though Zoe had found it, or more likely, had pulled it from our bin of gloves and scarves, and begun to chew on it. I took them off completely and tossed them in my bag. One more thing now added to my list of chores: repair glove.

At the first bus stop on Broadway a small group of elderly Asian women boarded. Each one took a painfully long time, placing their fare cards in the machine before sitting down in the seats designated for the disabled. I didn't feel like I was ever going to make it home. Once they were seated and the bus resumed its route the large man sitting in front of me picked himself up from his seat by pulling on the stop cord above. I was certain it was going to break due to the force he exerted, but it held tight. As the man anxiously climbed over the petite woman sitting next to him, I noticed he was wearing a simple t-shirt and denim jacket. It amazes me what some people will wear in twenty-degree weather. Fumbling to the rear exit after practically trampling the petite rider, the man withdrew a package of cigarettes and a small, green lighter. I knew what was coming next. I had seen it many, many times on the train, but rarely on a city bus. Before the exit doors had even opened, just prior to the man's departure, the lighter was ignited and the cigarette, poised outward in his lips, was being lit.

No sooner had the flame been revealed, than the petite woman began making coughing noises. This was her nonchalant way of saying, "Asshole." Not fazed by the fake hacking, the man with the cigarette bounded out the door as soon as the green light appeared, leaving a faint trail of smoke to linger and spread throughout the back of the bus. I still had another ten minutes before I was home. I considered getting off at the next stop and hailing a taxi. Checking my wallet for money, I came across three one-dollar bills. It occurred to me I should always carry enough cash for an emergency cab ride.

The snow was beginning to pick up and I began to worry that I wouldn't be able to get out of town if it became severe. There had been no report of inclement weather to speak of during the morning news, but knowing how inconsistent our weathermen are in Chicago, and viewing the unannounced snow before me, I was uncertain whether or not to expect accumulation. I had been planning this trip for a while and needed to speak to Brandi in person. I couldn't wait any longer.

To pass the time, I retrieved my cellphone once again and sent an emergency text message to Kory. "I'm in HELL!" An alert message popped up informing me of the low battery. I sat with the phone cupped in my hand and stared out the window, watching the lights of the traffic pass by at every intersection. At the corner of Foster and Ashland we stopped to pick up a man in a wheelchair. What in the world anyone was doing out in this weather in a wheelchair was beyond me. The driver opened the door and with a switch of a button began to lower the platform to the sidewalk. I paused my music to hear the muffled voices of the driver and the man outside the bus. It appeared as though he was having trouble rolling his chair onto the metal platform and the driver was not willing to assist. Finally, after a couple of minutes of trying, the bus driver stepped from his seat and began to pull the wheelchair onboard. A solid four minutes passed before the driver resumed his position at the wheel and the rider in the wheelchair was maneuvering his way to the front. Each of the four elderly Asian women, still seated, watched as the handicapped man boarded the bus and soon realized they would have to give up their seats in order for him to place his chair safely against the side of the bus.

My hand began to vibrate. I looked down at my phone and saw Kory's reply. "Sorry baby."

The Asian women were now standing and slowly making their way to the rear of the bus, staring at every passenger they passed in the hopes that each would surrender their own seats. I could see the lead senior heading my way and decided to relinquish my spot before her gaze pierced my eyes. Besides, there were only two more stops to go.

At Wolcott the entire rear of the bus decided at once to exit and forced me to move back up to the front of the bus. Like the train ride, I fumbled and stumbled over anyone standing in the aisle and everyone with their feet in the way. But I didn't care. The Damen stop was next. I reached over and pulled the cord.

When the doors opened I heard the driver caution me to watch my step. "Thanks," I replied. On the sidewalk I struggled to keep my balance. The thin coating of snow on the already-present icy ground was becoming a hazard.

Reaching the back door of our condo I scrambled to find the house key in my messenger bag. I could hear Zoe at the door, anticipating her nightly pee. I was well over an hour late and I figured she would be waiting with legs crossed. As soon as the key was in the hole and the door was ajar, she charged passed me and scurried down the back stairs. I tossed my bag on the counter, grabbed her leash and a poop bag, and ran down after her.

On the first landing I took a serious fall. I can only assume that the step was slick with snow. My feet flew out in front of me and I came down hard on my butt and right arm. I bounced down another three steps before I was able to grab onto the railing and stop myself from going further. "FUCK, FUCKER, FUCK!" I yelled. I was channeling Mr. Cellphone. Where was Zoe?

"Zoe!" I called after her.

I managed to pull myself up and lumber down the rest of the staircase, holding onto the railing for dear life. My arm was throbbing.

"Zoe!" I yelled again.

When I got to the bottom of the stairs, I caught Zoe looking back down the sidewalk towards me as if to see if I had made it. When she saw that I was not seriously hurt, she hurried off into the yard and squatted.

"Zoe, wait!" I called out to her. When I got to the end of the walkway, there she sat, in the middle of the front lawn relieving herself. I figured after hours of a stuffed bladder, she deserved to go wherever she could make it. I placed the leash on her collar, opened the front gate, and tried to get her to potty once more on the parkway. Since my arm was hurting and she refused to go, wanting only to play in the snow, I decided we should both go back upstairs. I had much more to do, but only wanted to lie down and take care of my arm.

After putting away my things, feeding Zoe, and tossing a load of dirty clothes in the laundry, I decided it was best to begin packing. Normally, it is out of character for me to be planning a trip to Glasgow this time of year. I usually only visit once either at Thanksgiving or Christmas, spending the other holiday with Kory's family in Reno.

I started to pack a duffle, deciding what to wear while I'd be away. It was February and I knew it could be cool, although the mildness of winter tends to appear much earlier in south central Kentucky than it does in Chicago. The region had recently experienced terribly destructive tornadoes as well, an unseasonable occurrence for the second month of the year. While making national news, CNN was reporting 57 lives lost due to the twisters.

At the same time, Chicago was experiencing its third round of snowstorms in as little as two weeks. We were now measuring snow in feet and, as I had experienced earlier, sliding on sidewalks caked with ice. Between the sleet, high winds, and below- freezing temperatures, I was beginning to dream of spring, but not a Chicago spring, a real spring. Spring in Chicago is over too quickly. When winter ends and the gray clouds make way for blue skies, Chicagoans may experience a week, perhaps two, of temperate weather, before quickly shifting into hot, muggy days. But the muggy days of Chicago certainly don't compare to the muggy days of Glasgow.

I have a bad habit of packing too much and regretting it once I've reached my destination. I pulled a plain, white button-down shirt out of the closet and stared at it as though it would reveal to me whether or not I should include it in my luggage. It answered yes. I struggled to fasten every button and clumsily folded it into a small package.

Normally I would have had Kory folding my clothes and organizing the suitcases, but tonight he wasn't around. Instead he was working; attending the opening night performance of *As You Like It*. Although he dislikes packing, I knew he would rather be here with me than at a job in which he was growing less fond. For months he had been trying to find an alternative employer. The two of us had just returned from a trip to Washington where he was in final talks with Seattle Rep to be their new director of marketing. They had flown me out as well to get a lay of the land and to woo us into moving, but after serious discussions and weighing the pros and cons, we decided to remain in Chicago. For me, it just didn't feel right and it was too difficult to explain to others why. But the beauty of Kory is that he knows me better than I know myself sometimes and that I don't always have to explain why. I was wishing he were here, not only to make sense of these unruly clothes, but also to comfort my nerves. I always find it a bit daunting going home.

"Home," I said aloud. I've not lived in Glasgow for over fifteen years and yet, somehow, I still referred to it as home. Even after I had left, I still considered it home. I held close ties. I was proud to talk about it, joked that it was the center of the universe. Everyone I seemed to meet from LA to New York City had either heard of it or knew of someone from there. If anything, I could always proclaim that Glasgow was the birthplace of journalist, Diane Sawyer – one of its very few claims to fame.

Yet over the last few years I had noticed that connection fading, and like my aversion to Seattle, I wasn't sure why. That closeness that I had once felt was shifting into that of antipathy. I have an affinity towards the South in general; to the traditions, the food, the charm and hospitality, but I found myself giving up on the characteristics Glasgow had to offer. I had struggled for some time to determine whether it was I that had changed or the town itself, but later realized that it didn't matter. This was how it was. This was how it was always going to be.

I tossed a belt from the closet towards the suitcase but missed. It slid off the bed and its buckle slammed onto the hardwood floor. Zoe came running into the bedroom to investigate the commotion and sprang upon the mattress. Suddenly, she grabbed one of my socks, resting on the edge of the case, in her mouth and rushed back out of the bedroom. Normally I would go, present her with a treat, and bargain with her to release it, but tonight I didn't bother. I had too much on my mind. In less than 48 hours

I would be interviewing Brandi and discussing her brother's tragic demise.

I flipped on the TV for background noise only to find that one of my favorite British import shows was currently on. *Most Haunted* is a supposedly non-fictional program where ghost hunters investigate haunted locations, primarily around the British Isles. The crew uses night-vision cameras while hunting for spirits and every episode of the show contains at least one ridiculously amusing scream from the show's host, Yvette. Kory and I also find it humorous each time the program's psychic medium uses the word "astral." One could accuse us of being immature. One would be correct.

I am fascinated by these types of programs, those that attempt to highlight the paranormal, particularly ghosts, but I also enjoy a good program about UFO's, angels, demons, and of course, Bigfoot. Little did I know at the time, but I would be presented with one of these paranormal entities during my investigation of Scotty's death and I wouldn't know what to make of it.

I started to think again about what I was going to say to Brandi when we met. Almost three weeks before, on a gloomy, gray Saturday, I had somehow gotten up the nerve to contact her in the hopes that she would meet with me to talk about her brother who had died approximately four years prior.

. . .

That particular Saturday afternoon had been the coldest day of the winter so far. Chicago had a high of five-degrees with wind chills of twenty-below. Unfortunately for Kory, he had to brave the weather and spend the day working in Glencoe. I was inside, warm and cozy, trying to pump myself up in an effort to make contact with Scotty's sister. Through a lot of digging around online I managed to eventually locate Brandi's email address and carefully began typing the letter that would hurdle me deeper into my investigation.

An hour into my correspondence I reflected back upon the text and decided to begin again. What I had written was not what I had wanted to say. I was trying to make contact with a person who may or may not have even remembered me in high school. Brandi is two years younger than I am and I wasn't quite sure if I had ever spoken to her before. My entire high school was no more than 400 students, but upper classmen weren't likely to interact with freshmen and sophomores. I ran to the guest bedroom and searched for a yearbook.

In a storage container under the bed I came across my annual from senior year as well as several theatre programs and newspaper clippings. One stood out in particular as I scanned the list of names under the dozens of black and white faces. For a performance of *Spoon River Anthology*, put on by the Speech and Drama department, I saw two faces in the crowd. On one end of the front row was mine; at the other end, Brandi Martin. I then grabbed the program that corresponded to the show to see what role she had been given. No role. Make-up. That would be my way in.

I headed back to my computer and started the lengthy letter over again. I mentioned the idea that she may not even remember me, although I found it a little absurd that a sophomore wouldn't remember a senior. They were supposed to look up to us, right? I reminded her of the play and suggested that she even did my make up as the old, Jewish man residing in Spoon River, made up entirely of Protestants. The character, long dead, recites a monologue and kvetches about living his entire life in a town where he never felt like he truly belonged. At the time I never acknowledged the irony, but it soon dawned on me while typing the email.

I continued to describe how Scotty and I had known each other better while in college than in high school. We used to see each other out at the bars and we would gossip about everyone else from Glasgow. And although I had intended to include it, I failed to mention that her brother and I had even dated the same guy.

Continuing on, I detailed the day I heard about Scotty's death. I told her of the afternoon phone call I received from my friend Susannah, also a native of Glasgow. It was the eleventh of June and I assumed she was phoning to wish me a happy birthday, but she never mentioned it. Instead the first words out of her mouth were "Scotty Martin is dead." Susannah went on to say that he had been in a coma for ten days since his high school reunion, and although there were rumors floating around town, no one knew exactly what had happened.

I wrote and wrote and wrote more and more, words pouring from my fingers to the keys and appearing on the screen. I let Brandi know how I never forgot the day Susannah called and how I felt haunted, for lack of a better word, by Scotty's passing. There had been rumors that he was the victim of a hate crime, left to die at the bottom of a concrete retaining wall after being attacked. I detailed my own personal story of growing up gay in the small Kentucky town that we shared and expressed sympathy for knowing all too well the familiar perils.

Lastly, before I put forth my request for a meeting, I described how it was more than Scotty's death that had troubled me for almost four years. I admitted how I felt betrayed by Glasgow when no indictments came about from Scotty's case and repulsed that his memory was quickly swept under the rug. My eyes began to tear up as I typed, so I pushed the laptop away and broke the connection I had with the keys and my words. I knew then that I was doing the right thing.

After hand picking each word and rewriting the email over and over again, I could no longer think of any more or any less to say. It was time to hit "Send." But I stalled. I stared out the window for another half hour before I re-read it. All in all, it had taken me over four hours (most of the afternoon) to compose the perfect email. And while I danced around, considering all the reasons not to send it to her, I finally garnered all the strength I had remaining to release it into cyberspace.

I sat there in front of the computer for a while longer thinking about what I had just done. I couldn't believe this was really happening. I kept playing out scenarios in my head. She'd read my letter, wonder who the hell I was and if I was serious, before sending my email to the trash. Or she would read the letter and think I had less than good intentions before reporting me to the police. Then I thought of the possibility that it was much too painful still and she only wanted to forget what had happened.

Now here I was, reminding her of this tragic experience and asking her to relive it. What had I done?

No sooner had I wondered aloud about my deed than I heard a noise from my computer. *Ding.* I had received an email. Could it have been her responding? It had been fifteen minutes since sending it from my end; plenty of time to read and refuse my request. My nerves got the better of me. I was too afraid to look at the screen. I hopped around the room with butterflies in my stomach. What had I just done? I started wishing I had never written the email, much less sent it to her. I called Kory's phone. No answer. I wanted him to get home right away so he could check my inbox for me and read what she had replied. I was too much of a chicken to look.

Two and a half hours later, Kory finally arrived. I still hadn't gone near the computer. Quickly I welcomed him home with a kiss, grabbed his arm, rushed him to the desk and asked to read the reply that had been causing me such anxiety.

He read it forthright, "Failed delivery."

I rolled my eyes and screamed, "WHAT?!" I couldn't believe it. All this time I had worried about an email sent into the unknown and back again. I read the response closer. The address I had for Brandi was no good. I realized I had to start all over again.

. . .

Back in the bedroom, I had finished gathering all the clothes I thought I would wear while I was away. I wanted to look professional when I met with Brandi, so I managed to pick out a conservative outfit I felt would make me look like a serious writer. From my closet I chose a white-collar dress shirt, gray cashmere sweater vest, cotton dress pants, with a striped ribbon belt and black loafers. I arranged the pieces on the bed as if a flat, invisible man were wearing them all and then heard Kory's voice in my head. *"Why are you taking those clothes? We're only going to Glasgow."* And with that thought, I immediately returned the items back into the closet and tossed a pair of denim jeans in my duffle.

Along with my clothes, I had placed a number of other items beside the bag that I wanted to remember to take with me. I had my notebook set aside with pages and pages of questions, a folder stuffed with articles and other information I had printed from the internet, and a copy of the day's *Tribune*. I happened to glance down at the paper and read a headline that I hadn't noticed earlier. "Oxnard School Shooting Called a Hate Crime." The headline grabbed my attention for two reasons. One was the obvious announcement of a hate crime, but the other was the fact that I had lived in Oxnard, California after graduating from college. I rarely saw the name mentioned but took notice when it was.

According to the article, a 15-year-old boy was shot in the head by a classmate after the victim proclaimed himself gay and asked the shooter to be his Valentine. My stomach dropped. I read further. Lawrence King, the victim, was declared brain-dead and expected to be taken off life support so his organs could be donated. My mind raced. What was this world coming to? I could only think that this was happening at the same time I was beginning to write a book about another possible hate crime. Through a blog she had written online, I knew Brandi had kept up to date with the Natalee Holloway incident, as it happened a year to the day that Scotty's body was found. It, too, was unsolved. I wondered if she had heard about this recent bit of news out of California.

...

The Monday following my first attempt to contact Brandi was Martin Luther King, Jr. Day. It was so cold that a water pipe in our laundry room had burst and Kory stayed home to wait for the plumber to come and fix it. I had to go to work because I had given my assistant the day off since I would be leaving town for Seattle that weekend. Though it sounded tempting, I kept thinking that moving that far away would make it harder for me to write my book, or at least more difficult to travel to Kentucky to research it. I was kicking myself for waiting as long as I did to begin writing.

At work I found Brandi again through Myspace.com and decided to email her from Kory's account, as I didn't have one. And for a second day, I rang my hands in anticipation of her response. I suddenly felt like I had just asked out the cutest boy in school and was suspended in that moment between asking and rejection.

Throughout the day, I found myself constantly clicking the "Send/Receive" button on my computer, waiting for a reply. None would come. Not until the evening of the following day would my stomach once again drop after seeing Brandi's name in my mailbox. I was, again, too scared to view her reply, but pulled myself together and began reading. There was no formal greeting; in fact, no greeting at all. Her response to me simply began:

I would like to ask you a few questions when you get a chance. You can email me back and let me know when you will be available or you can just call me. One concern at this point is my mother. She doesn't know anything about my efforts with the case and I don't intend for her to know what you are doing just yet. You see, since Scotty died, I have worked very hard at protecting my mother. Being a mother myself, I cannot imagine her personal hell, but I can see it in her eyes. We talk about Scotty daily and that is therapeutic for her... naming names, pointing fingers and discussing the latest rumors are destructive and I just simply refuse to let my mother go through anything unnecessary. My mother believes, as I do, that God will punish whoever is responsible, if anyone, for Scotty's death. However, my mother has more patience and virtue than I and she can wait until God's judgment...I can't. If I don't uncover the truth and expose it, I will never be at peace. Scotty would have fought to the very end for me and I intend to do the same for him.

Hope to hear from you soon.

Brandi

I finished reading the email and decided to give it a second look. I didn't know what to think. I couldn't tell if I had offended her or simply given hope, but I quickly realized that at this point, there was no turning back. I sat back in my chair and got chills.

Over the next several days, Brandi and I continued to keep in touch through emails and phone calls. We agreed upon a date in February to finally meet face to face. During this time I also made an open records request with the Kentucky State Police to obtain any and all records pertaining to Scotty's case. The month before I had contacted the Kentucky State Medical Examiner's Office for his autopsy and toxicology reports. I had never done anything like this before and wasn't sure if I was even doing it the proper way. I wasn't even sure if his case was still open or not. In the event that they were still investigating his death, there would be no chance of me getting any document whatsoever.

Within a few days of faxing my requests I received a call on my cellphone while I was at work. I didn't recognize the number on my caller ID, so I let it go into voicemail. When I retrieved the message, I heard the following:

"Kevin Troxall, this is Abigail Campbell with the Kentucky Medical Examiner's Office. Please call me back regarding your request for records for Scotty Martin."

In the research I had read prior to sending out my requests, it was noted that no one is allowed to contact you by phone once they receive your fax, so I found it very intriguing (in an espionage kind of way) that this Abigail person had called me. Instead of waiting around, I called her right back to see what she wanted.

"May I speak to Abigail Campbell please?" I asked.

"This is Abigail," the voice on the other end replied.

"Hi, this is Kevin Troxall from Chicago. I was returning your call from earlier."

"Yes, are you calling from an attorney's office?" I was asked.

I wasn't sure where we were going with the conversation so far, but I could only think the worst. Maybe the way I had made the request was not the proper method after all, and now I was about to be reprimanded somehow for it. Or maybe, I thought, this Abigail person was calling to tell me that I could only obtain information if I was a lawyer. Or just maybe she wanted to know if I worked in the legal field so she could reveal some secret intelligence that no one in the public sector knew about.

I answered with, "No."

"Is this the Kevin Troxall from Glasgow?" she then asked.

Now I began to panic. Suddenly, I surmised, I was on some government list and was about to be warned, *"If you know what's good for you, stop investigating the Scotty Martin case."*

I had to say something. "Yes," I mumbled. I was fearful about what she would say next.

"Kevin, this is Abigail Winwright from Glasgow."

"ABIGAIL! Oh my God, how are you?"

I was quickly relieved. Abigail Winwright and I graduated high school together. I hadn't thought about her in fifteen years and here she was on the other end of my phone, working for the state medical examiner.

"What is this about Scotty Martin? What are you doing?" she asked.

I went on to explain to her that I was researching his death and was gathering as much information as I could get my hands on. Being from the area, she obviously knew about the case.

"Well first of all we don't have those documents," she began. "He died at Vanderbilt so you'll have to contact the medical examiner's office in Tennessee."

Damn, I thought. "So what do you know about this case?" I was curious to hear from another outsider's perspective.

The same things everybody else has heard probably. You know Glasgow, small town and all. I heard Scotty was chased by some of the guys from his reunion because he had come on to 'em. Next mornin' they found his body lying by a loading dock."

"Do you remember who the guys were that you heard chased him?"

Abigail was silent for a minute. I could tell she was trying to think of names.

"No, I can't think of 'em right now. I wanna say Blake Oliver was one of 'em though, and maybe what's-his-name...Marrs."

Though I didn't respond I was suddenly perplexed by what Abigail had just said. I, too, had heard mention of Blake Oliver, but Marrs? Who could she be talking about? Benji Marrs? He was a classmate of Scotty's, but this was the first time I had ever heard mention of his name and was frankly puzzled. Benji was not at all the type of person I thought would be tied into such a situation.

Abigail continued on, "Right after he died, I was hopin' that we'd get the body so I could find out more about it. But like I said, they ended up doin' the autopsy in Nashville 'cause that's where he died."

"Do you think I should contact the medical examiner's office or Vanderbilt directly?" I asked.

"No, you'll want to call the medical examiner. I'd love to see that report though. I've always thought his case was pretty fishy and I had forgotten about it until I saw the request come in from you. I hope you find out what happened."

This was the first time anyone had said that to me and I felt a small sense of optimism, like I was doing the right thing. This feeling would come and go throughout the next few months, and eventually I would reach hopelessness and begin to abandon the investigation all together.

"Abigail," I began again, "I don't even know if this case is closed or not. I don't know how to find out."

"Have you talked to Brandi yet? I'm sure she'll know."

I explained, "No, I wanted to get access to records first before I start talking to Scotty's family."

"Well let me know if I can help out somehow. Good luck."

I hung up the phone, still perplexed about this new name, Marrs. For an hour I went about my routine and finally it started to make its way back into the forefront of my mind. Who the hell was she talking about? I had to know. So I decided to call her back again. Thankfully, I would receive good news.

"Abigail Campbell," I heard her answer.

"Hey Abigail, it's Kevin again. Earlier you mentioned the last name Marrs, and I'm trying to figure out who you were talking about?"

"Oh what's-his-name?" Abigail was just as bad at remembering people from high school as I was.

"Benji Marrs," I suggested.

"Oh no, not Benji. Uh…" she thought some more. "I can't think of it right now."

"That's okay. I was just curious if you meant Benji or not."

"No not Benji. If I think of it I'll let you know," she finished.

"Great. Thanks." I started to hang up.

"Hey wait," she exclaimed. "Scotty's case is closed."

"What?!" A glimmer of hope was on the horizon.

Abigail went on to explain that when their office gets an open records request, they are required to contact the state police. "And when I mentioned his case to the woman," Abigail said, "she told me that it was closed. So you should be able to get those records."

I was thrilled. "Thank you so much," I told Abigail. This time, after hanging up, I did a happy dance. Things were looking up.

. . .

After I finished packing for the trip to Glasgow I started going through my notes again. I wanted to be sure I had all the questions prepared to ask Brandi when we met. I flipped through the archived copies of news clippings, reviewed blogs written on Glasgow's online forum about Scotty, and studied the autopsy report that had finally arrived the day before. I even wrote down every bit of hearsay I had been told three years prior to possibly help separate fact from fiction.

In those notes, I wrote that Scotty attended his tenth year high school reunion on May 29, 2004. Supposedly he was being harassed during the event for being gay. On the morning after, his unconscious body was found by the loading dock that leads into the kitchen at the Lodge of the State Park. Blood was coming from his head, and, strangely, a wet rag was nearby, possibly to help stop the bleeding. After he was found, his body was flown to Vanderbilt Hospital where he died ten days later. Four guys were under suspicion for causing his injuries and possibly a couple of them had been caught in an uncompromising position with him, which led to the attack.

When the investigation began, I continued noting, the Parks Department initially handled it, but finding themselves in over their heads, and with the International Highland Games being held at the State Park the following weekend, they quickly cleaned up the scene and passed the case off to state police. In turn, the lead detective would declare publicly that the case was botched from the beginning. In September, a grand jury returned no indictments or true bills and Scotty's case abruptly ended.

Once I had finished jotting down my memories of the case, I unintentionally scribbled "The End" and sat my pen down. I stared at the two words, my fingers drumming beside them.

"The End." I expected the words to move.

The more I scrutinized them, the more I began to envision the email I had used to court Brandi into granting me an interview.

Hi Brandi-

This is Kevin Troxall. I'm not sure if you remember me, but not only am I from Glasgow too, but I believe you were in Speech & Drama with me my junior and senior years, and I'm almost positive you did my make-up for that God-awful Spoon River Anthology *at the Plaza Theatre. That's something I'd like to forget!*

That being said, the reason I am contacting you now is because I am a writer here in Chicago and have been working on research for a story about the investigation (or lack thereof) surrounding Scotty's death. I grew to know Scotty better when I was at UK. We'd see each other around the bars of Lexington and it was always fun to gossip about the people we both knew from Glasgow (i.e. who was gay or who was pretending not to be). I even had a crush on his roommate, James, at the time, so it was especially fun when I got to hang out at Scotty's apartment.

As it sometimes happens in life, we lost touch. I moved to New York City after leaving Lexington and never moved back to Kentucky. For the past nine years I've been in Chicago. My best friend, Susannah Kilbourne (whom you may remember as well) was the one who called and informed me of Scotty's passing on June 11...my birthday. Needless to say, I was taken aback to hear the news.

Since that day his passing has gripped me in a way I find difficult to explain. I live 400 miles away and have few ties to Glasgow anymore. What I heard about Scotty's death were snippets of news reports from The Glasgow Daily Times *online or hearsay that Susannah might have heard from her family. But what has affected me most is the lack of resolution and the feeling that my hometown has turned a blind eye towards one of its own.*

I know firsthand what it's like to grow up gay in a small town in the Bible Belt. I've experienced the frustration of having to conceal my true self from my family and closest friends, the hardship of coming out, and the overwhelming sense of relief of acceptance. I also understand what it's like to be hated for being yourself. And I've never felt more hated than the day I heard there were no indictments brought about for your brother.

They say each of us has a calling from God, and until recently, I think I've been ignoring mine. I never imagined in my wildest dreams that I would be contacting you or proposing his story be told publicly.

But here I am today, asking you to honor my request for an interview; to speak with me about your brother and help me make a difference. I understand that you've been quite outspoken about this case and are a major advocate for Scotty's memory. I can't promise you that I'll uncover anything you don't already know, but I guarantee that I won't let anyone forget him or forget how our legal system failed him.

And I can't imagine what you must be thinking about all this right now. Who is this nut contacting me out of the blue? I assure you that I don't mean to upset you if I have. I only want the best for you and for Scotty's memory. I give you my word, from one former GHS speech & drama student to another.

Thank you for taking the time to read this and I hope to hear from you soon.

Best regards,

Kevin

At that moment I was immediately aware I had to honor my word, so I picked up the pen again. I quickly crossed out the two words staring back at me and changed them to reflect the feeling of hope now at hand. In capital letters I wrote, "THE BEGINNING."

Two

While driving into Glasgow, I suddenly understand the saying, *"The more things change, the more they stay the same."* The landscape in which I now end my car ride is the complete opposite of the landscape from where I began. There are no skyscrapers, no hordes of tourists blocking the sidewalks, and certainly no bumper-to-bumper traffic. Yet, for some reason this really pisses me off. Where's the anonymity? Where's the constant white noise in the air that keeps me calm and feeling safe? And why do I suddenly feel like more eyes are staring at me here in a town whose population is 1% that of Chicago? Later, when I have ended this journey completely, I will face the realization that I hate this town. But for now, I simply dislike it. A lot.

Driving on Highway 90 is the route of my arrival into Glasgow. This stretch of pavement will turn into Happy Valley Road, an ironic name for such a dispiriting expansion of terrain. With its empty store fronts and used car lots, the road has lost its economic appeal that it once held in years past. The current hub of Glasgow's commerce sits in the far northern section of the town in a sprawl of businesses anchored by an impressive Wal-Mart Supercenter. The featureless buildings that make up this collection of a strip mall see an abundance of local traffic, as there is very little to do elsewhere in town except congregate here. The days of unique mom-and-pop shops are long gone, most notably in the town's public square where every other building is home to an attorney's office. It was barely two decades ago when the square was a bustling center of shopping. You could find local townspeople eating their lunches at George J's and catching up on local politics seated next to the mayor or taking in a matinee showing of the latest movie at the Plaza Theatre with its prominent red and yellow marquee.

Back on Highway 90, I pass the monstrous Wal-Mart on my right. Across the road is Glasgow's only movie theater, a noticeable improvement since I resided here. I am actually surprised to see that all eight screens are showing the latest Hollywood films. South of the cinema is Border's Monuments, the local source for quality tombstones. When I was much younger this building housed the local skating rink. Times have certainly changed.

I pass a large billboard in the distance. Planted in an empty tobacco field it reads, "Jesus Loves You. John 3:16." I scratch my head wondering who the hell constructed that sign and if they know they've misquoted that particular verse. Another saying crosses my mind. "*Ignorance is bliss.*" I continue on through the outskirts of town toward the public square and start to approach my destination.

When I pulled into the parking lot, I hadn't yet decided how I was going to greet Brandi. This was a woman I can't say I ever spoke to in high school and until a few weeks before, I had no idea whether or not she would ever want to meet with me under these circumstances. Was shaking hands too businesslike? Was a hug too personal? Maybe I do nothing and simply say hello and thanks. I took out my water bottle and had a sip. My throat was a little dry.

Glancing around, I hoped that I was in the right place. I saw a blue minivan coming up behind me and pull off to the side of the street. I never thought to take her as a soccer mom, but there she was. As a thirty-two year old with no children who relishes television and pop culture, I have no grasp of what people my age and younger with families are like. In my mind, I'm still seventeen years old and the thought of any of my peers with kids just doesn't process. I simply refuse to grow up.

I stepped out of my car and watched as Brandi climbed out of the van, then crossed the street towards me. She looked nothing like I remember and yet, everything like Scotty. She was smiling. She wore no makeup but her complexion was flawless and her hair was glowing in the sunlight. She was both simple and stunning, practically angelic.

"Am I late?" she asked. I was immediately taken in by her accent because it sounded like my mother's, familiar and comforting, not too pronounced. Most people never figure I'm from Kentucky because of my own cadence. "*Why don't you have an accent?*" is something I'm frequently asked when introduced to others. I explain that I was a theatre major and worked hard to get rid of it; one less obvious tie to my roots. But Brandi's voice suited her well; certain and unyielding with a true South Central Kentucky lilt. She left the "g" off words like "coming" and "going" so they came off as innocent, down-home expressions like "comin' and goin'."

Responding to her question, I answered, "Not at all." I leaned towards her with open arms. We embraced quickly. "How are you?" I asked nervously.

"Good," she replied.

For a few seconds I wasn't sure what was happening. It didn't seem real, and yet, I had to convince myself to focus and express confidence. I was here for a reason.

Brandi took out a key and opened the door to a friend's business; a location I would later be asked to keep secret. "There's a few people I don't think would be happy if they knew we were meetin' here."

"Why?" I asked naively, realizing the answer to my question as soon as I spoke.

"It's Glasgow. Everybody's tied in to everybody else around here. It just wouldn't look good. Now let's get inside."

I followed Brandi in and toward a small room in the rear of the building. There was already a small table with two chairs waiting for us like someone knew we were coming. I set down the bag I had brought filled with papers and a notebook containing the questions I was here to ask.

Brandi placed her purse on the table and pulled out her cellphone. She removed her sunglasses and I could see her eyes for the first time. Now she looked even more like her brother.

I sat down in one of the chairs and fumbled with a few papers while Brandi sat in the chair directly across from mine. She watched as I continued gathering my papers in order and searched for a pen with which to write.

"My mom doesn't approve that I'm here," she blurted out.

I ceased floundering with my notes and looked up at her quizzically. "You told her you were meeting with me?"

She nodded. "I decided to be honest with her. I told her I had started to look into Scotty's case again 'cause there were things I needed to know."

"And you obviously told her I was writing a book?" I asked, again knowing the answer.

"Um hmmm," she hummed.

"What does she think of that?" I asked.

Brandi shrugged. "Her biggest concern is that somethin's gonna get twisted or make him appear in a way that he wasn't. She could care less if we find out what happened to him. It's not gonna bring him back. She can live with that. I can't."

I could begin to see the determination in her eyes. I could also see the pain.

"She doesn't feel like it's necessary to try and find out what happened," she continued. "She doesn't feel like writin' a book is necessary. She doesn't feel like anything is necessary 'cause none of it's gonna bring him back. She also believes that if anybody had anything to do with it, obviously, the Lord is gonna take care of that in the end."

Brandi had mentioned to me in an earlier email that her mom was a spiritual woman and was leaving this into the hands of God. I was struggling to comprehend her ideology. How could any mother not wish to learn the truth about the mysterious death of her own child? I scribbled a word into my notes. *Faith*.

"I told her I trusted you and I know you have good intentions," she said. Hearing that from Brandi made me want to jump across the table and kiss her.

"Absolutely," I said. "You have no idea how difficult that first email to you was to write!"

She agreed, "I know, and then my reply was like, '*Oh my God, I love you!*' She laughed. "It's always helped me to have people to talk about it. I have three young kids, obviously I can't talk to. I have a husband who didn't even know him. I have my mom who I don't want to upset. So to me, when somebody approaches and says, 'I knew Scotty' or 'I liked Scotty,' I eat it up!" She smiled, which then made me smile.

"I was afraid that you might not even want to talk about it," I admitted.

"I've always talked about it," she said. "Right after it happened there was a period of time where I was just there for my mom. You know, it was really sad, and suddenly I was an only child. She was so fragile. I had to be there for her. But it was hard for me too. At the time, I was a single mom with two kids and I was strugglin'. I wasn't sleepin' and I was havin' panic attacks. I would lie awake at night with my hands on each kid and just count breaths, all night. I was on medicine to sleep, I was on medicine to live, to stay awake, to get through the day…it was just too much. And finally I thought, I've got to get myself together, so I started goin' to church and I met my husband, Josh. And I had my mom in the background saying, 'I don't want anybody to solve it, I don't want anything to happen, God'll take care of it, let's just live.' So that's what I did. I got remarried, I had a baby, but the more time that goes on, I feel like this is the right time to try and figure it out. And I'm not tryin' to do it against her wishes, but for myself and for my sanity. I just really need to know."

I nodded. "A lot of people want to know. That's why I'm doing this."

She continued on, "If I didn't have a job or anything else to do and could devote my time to it, I would. But I could drive myself crazy with it, honestly. A lot of times it's all I think about. And yet I can't even dream about it. I go to bed at night and pray that I'll dream about it. Just show me a dream. Just show me what happened. Give me some peace. You know, not knowin' is torture."

I started to lean in towards the table and caught myself grasping every word she spoke. This is why I had come to Glasgow, I thought. Unaware to me at the time, I too would be driven crazy by what happened, but unlike Brandi, I *would* have dreams about it, nightmares even.

"I'm a little different than my mom," she explained. "I got my dad's patience, or lack of. Scotty had her patience. He was just like her, so calm. Me? I need to know everything now! But my dad worried himself to death over it, literally. Eleven months after Scotty died, he died of a massive heart attack. Fifty-one years old. He had other health problems that contributed to that too, but Scotty's death didn't help the situation. He really worried himself to death wonderin' what happened."

"Was he aware of *everything*?" I asked, trying in the most sensitive way to question if her dad had known Scotty was gay. I hate speaking in code, but in Glasgow I was no longer protected by the safe, invisible walls of urban culture where you needn't worry to whisper the word *gay* in public.

"Yes," she answered. "And people who knew my father would tell you that if he had known he was only gonna live eleven more months, he'd have killed 'em all with his hands; anybody they suspected was involved. He would have hunted all of 'em down, whether they did it or not, and killed 'em if he knew he wasn't gonna live much longer." She smiled again, suspiciously. "Daddy and Scotty had just gotten together. It had taken all these years and they had just gotten on common ground. Daddy was doin' great. He'd go visit Scotty in Bowling Green, and they'd talk on the phone. It was like they finally had it together and then they lost it. And it just killed him. He had a lot of guilt. He prayed a lot. He just…it just killed him. It did."

I asked to change the subject a bit and questioned Brandi about growing up in Glasgow; more specifically about her childhood with her brother.

"I called him Mama's Boy!" She laughed loudly. I started to chuckle. "He was the perfect child. He was a straight-A student, never got into trouble. Pissed me off!"

I could tell she was enjoying talking about him.

"We didn't have money growin' up, so I shared a bedroom with him my whole life," she explained. "And I hated every minute of havin' to share a bedroom with him! But I think everything we went through as children led us to be as close as we were as adults. We used to fight, and now that I'm a mother and have kids, I understand what my mom went through. I didn't make good grades, and for a long time I think it was just jealousy. I was a year behind him in school, so when I got the teachers he had just had, all I heard from them was, 'Oh, your brother!'"

"So much to live up to, huh?" I asked.

"And I never lived up to it!" We laughed together.

I explained to her that my sister and I weren't close throughout high school either and it wasn't until after both of us had gone through college that we became as close as we were today.

"We would pass each other in the hall. I mean, it wasn't cool to hang out in the hall with your brother. But after he went to college and I had to live without him, I realized I missed him." She joked, "I thought I didn't like him and then I realized I loved him."

"What about living here," I began, "I mean, you live in Bowling Green now, but how did you feel at the time about living in Glasgow?"

"I didn't know anything else. Glasgow was just…Glasgow," she said.

"How do you feel about it now," I asked.

Matter-of-factly and without missing a beat she said, "I live in Bowling Green now." No one had to explain what she meant by that.

"I actually moved there after all of this happened to be closer to my mother. And in the process of lookin' for somewhere to live, I actually met my husband, and he happened to be from Bowling Green, so I stayed in Glasgow until we married and then we moved in together. But I'm glad to be out of Glasgow. I feel like I was let down. We were let down here. It was really disappointing."

I could certainly empathize with what Brandi was describing and understood completely that same disappointment.

I started to change the subject again. "Did Scotty officially come out to you?"

"No, he never did. I just always knew. You know, at some point everybody in the band gets labeled," she started to explain.

I quickly chimed in, "And the theatre department too."

"Right. You know, whether it's true or not, kids are cruel. I've heard my son say, 'I can't wear those shorts because they come above the knee and if you don't wear shorts below the knee, you're gay.' I said, 'Where did you hear that? Do you know what gay means? Gay means happy, so if wearin' short shorts makes you happy, honey wear 'em!'"

I burst out with laughter. Her brash wit was gratifying and I could clearly picture the scene in my mind. It was hilarious. Yet as quickly as I had envisioned that sight, my mind filled with the image of Lawrence King from Oxnard and I stopped laughing.

"That word gets thrown around so loosely," Brandi explained, "and it's really not in their vocabulary. I remember when I was little, a kid on the bus used to tell me that my brother was gay, and I would say, 'No, he's not!' And at the time I didn't know what *gay* was. To me it was just the same thing my kid thinks it is, meanin' not cool or lame."

"Sure," I agreed.

"Or different. Somethin' different. It wasn't a positive word, so I defended him and would say 'No he's not, no he's not.' And then I'd go home and think about it. What was he talkin' about? Why was he sayin' that about Scotty? And when we got older, Scotty dated girls, so I thought, well maybe he's not. Then they'd break up and he didn't seem to care about it. I think those were the times he was really confused and tryin' to figure out who he was and if these feelings he had were right. And then when we were adults we talked about it, and he said he knew from the sandbox. And it didn't change anything. He was my brother and I loved him unconditionally."

"Was it different for him in Lexington?" I asked.

"When he was in Lexington, he was totally out. Open. Honest. And when he would come back to Bowling Green he knew he had to be careful about the things he said. We always had this obsession with protectin' our mother. We didn't like to talk about the bad things we did because we held her in such high respect our whole lives. We didn't want her to think bad about us, you know, and we didn't want to talk about things that might change her opinion. But I know now that it doesn't matter. She knew about Scotty. I don't know when she found out, but she knew and she didn't care. It was just somethin' we didn't talk about. We didn't talk about how straight I was!"

It was comforting to see the humor in Brandi's life and I could tell she wasn't the guarded person I thought she might be.

"The fact that Scotty was gay is just a small part of who he was. He was my best friend, my brother. He didn't care what I did in my personal life and I didn't care what he did in his. It didn't change anything."

I was impressed with this tender indifference. Times have surely changed, but I'm always leery of others' attitudes towards the subject of homosexuality here in the conservative South, which brought me to my next question for her.

"Did you ever worry about him being gay?"

"Um…," she started to answer then stopped to ponder what I had just asked.

I modified the question. "Probably more so in Bowling Green than in Lexington?"

She chimed in, "Oh no. I worried more about him in Lexington."

"Really!" I thought her reply was peculiar. Personally, I would find it much easier to be out in the bigger city of Lexington.

"Because I didn't know what he was doin'," she explained. "I didn't know where he was. In the back of my mind I knew it was a lot easier in Lexington to actually be himself. I knew he was happy, I knew he was comfortable. But I know how things can get when you're in a place where you can do anything and say anything and be anything you want to be."

Brandi continued to explain herself, but I was fixated on what she had just said. I thought to myself, wouldn't it be great if we could all live that way. To be able to be the person we wanted to be without limitations? To express ourselves and live the life we felt we were meant to live? To love the people we chose to love without fear?

"I felt sorry for him because he couldn't totally be himself," she added.

When she said that, I immediately understood what she had meant. There are always risks around those who choose to be themselves.

"It's not really socially acceptable in Bowling Green," she said, eyebrows raised.

"Yeah, there's no gay pride parade marching down Scottsville Road," I joked.

Brandi grinned, "No, they wouldn't do that."

"Was he dating anyone at the time?"

"He never dated people publicly," she answered. "I'm sure he did in Lexington, but after he moved to Bowling Green he didn't date publicly. If he did date, nobody knew it. I think he may have met people online. He was so private with his private life. He was the most private person in the world. If I were to bring it up, he'd talk about it, but he never brought up anything."

I quickly remembered one of the rumors I had heard weeks after he died. Supposedly Scotty had approached one or two of his straight, male classmates during the reunion and made sexual advances toward them. To me, that scenario didn't seem like something someone so private would do.

Brandi went on, "He knew my mom knew, but we didn't talk about things like that. I didn't talk to her about dates and sex and he wasn't gonna tell her either! We just had that level of respect for Momma. I just felt like he was on his best behavior when he lived closer."

Brandi continued to talk about Scotty's life in Bowling Green. "All he did was go to work. He'd save his money. He wanted to buy a Volkswagen Bug and he was savin' money for this Bug. He had this piece of junk car that was always tore up. He even moved closer to where he worked so he could walk. He went out with me every Friday night 'cause I was divorced and I didn't have anything to do. Then we went out with my mom on Sundays. We just had our quaint, little life, so I didn't worry about him, but it bothered me that I knew…" Brandi stopped. She had a look of remorse on her face. "He was happy to a certain extent. I knew he would've been happier if he had had a date and could go out and enjoy it instead of sneakin' away or chit-chattin' on the computer."

I was beginning to see sympathy in her expression and I could feel it in her words.

"I wish he could have been more open about it. I wish it were more accepted so he could have been."

The mood in the room suddenly became more somber and I was reluctant to change the subject once again, especially towards the night of the reunion, but I was here to find out as much as I could and we only had a couple of hours to speak.

"Did Scotty talk to you about attending the reunion?"

She surprised me with her answer. "Yeah, he wasn't goin'."

"Really!" I said loudly. I think my reaction startled her as much as her reply shocked me.

"No," she said, laughing at my outburst. "That's one of the things that has always bothered me, because he *wasn't* going." She continued to reveal more. "He would go to the mall, and in the course of a year he ran into so many people from school that he hadn't seen in years. People, he told me, that he loved and missed. So when the reunion came about, he said, 'I'm not gonna go. I've run into everybody that I care to see and I'm not goin'. Plus, it's in Barren County and I don't have a way to get there.' Like I said, his car was broken down, but he didn't have his license at the time either. He walked everywhere. He lived close enough to work, but he'd walk to the mall and walk to the grocery. All that walkin' did him good; he was in great shape, physically."

At the time I didn't ask, and I wasn't sure if it mattered, but I quickly jotted another note. *No license.*

"So I didn't hear any more about the reunion until that Saturday mornin'. It was Memorial Day weekend, the kids were at their dad's, and I had a barbecue to go to with some of my friends. And so Scotty called me that mornin' and said, 'Go with me. I wanna go.' And at first I said, 'No, they are gonna ream you for goin' to your reunion with your sister.'" Brandi and I both laughed at the suggestion. "And he said, 'I don't care what they think, you're goin' with me.' And then I told him I had plans with my friends and he said, 'I don't care. I'm goin' no matter what. If you don't come take me, I'm gonna get a cab. I've called and it's $80 to go from here to the State Park.'"

Again, I scribbled what Brandi had just said. *Eighty dollars.*

She continued her story. "He was so persistent. I asked him, 'What is wrong with you? Why do you have to go?' And he said, 'I'm just goin'. I just want to go.'"

Brandi put her arms on the table and placed her head in her hands looking downward as if she were about to pray.

"You know, that's one thing over the years I have always thought about. Why all of a sudden did he have to go? He had no interest in goin' and now he's goin' no matter what." At this point Brandi returned her gaze, hands cupped in her chin, as if she were looking to me for the answer. Unfortunately, I didn't have one.

"So how did he get there," I asked.

"My ex-sister-in-law took him," she said. "He called me back to say he had gotten a ride. He said some of the others had rented cabins at the Park too, and if he couldn't find a ride home, he'd spend the night. So I told him I would come pick him up in the mornin'. I asked, 'What time do you want me to call?' and he said, 'Call me at 8:00 a.m.' I said, 'Fine, I'll call you at 8:00 a.m.'"

Another note written. *8:00 a.m.*

"So he went, and I went to the barbecue, and later that night I got a call from my dad. He said, 'What's the matter? Where's Scotty?'"

Brandi took a deep breath and explained, "It's weird. It's kinda like we had a sign that somethin' was happenin' before it happened. My dad was freakin' out 'cause he couldn't get ahold of him, and I said, 'Scotty's at his reunion. He probably can't hear his phone ring or he might have turned it off.' My dad was livin' in Florida at the time. He said, 'Well I'm worried about him.' And I told him that I was gonna go pick him up in the mornin' and I'd have Scotty call him then."

At this point Brandi described her evening at the barbecue. She told me she had decided to spend the night at her friend's house.

"It started rainin' about three or four o'clock in the mornin'. Rain doesn't usually keep me awake, but that night I heard every drop that hit the ground. Plus, I wasn't in my own bed, so I decided to leave and got home around 6:30 a.m. or 7:00 a.m. As soon as I got home, my mom called. We spoke every Sunday and she was callin' to check in before she left for church. She asked if I had heard from Scotty, and I told her I was gonna go pick him up when he called. So I hung up, and all I wanted to do was go to sleep, but I figured I'd wait for him to call. And I didn't hear anything so I started to text his cellphone. Never heard from him. Then I got a call from Amy, my ex-sister-in-law, who took him to the Park."

I found out from Brandi that she and Amy were friends before Brandi married her brother. One of Amy's best friends, Erin Gibson, was also at the reunion with Scotty.

"Amy told me," Brandi started, "that Erin was about to call me and I better pick it up. Well I thought that was odd. Why would Erin Gibson be callin' me? Erin works for child protection so I immediately thought, 'Oh my God, what has my ex-husband done? They're gonna take my kids away!' So I told Amy, "I don't want to talk to Erin Gibson. What does she want?' All Amy could say is, 'She's about to call you, and you have to pick up the call.' Then my other line started ringin'.'"

During this account I felt like I was reading a mystery novel. The setup was slow and gradual, but I knew at any second now the shoe was about to fall. Sadly, this was no fictional story and the ground beneath Brandi was about to open up and swallow her whole.

"I kept resisting," she said, "and finally Amy yelled at me, 'Dammit Brandi, something's happened to Scotty and you need to answer your phone!'"

I discovered my own chin now resting inside cupped hands, listening intently.

"Erin was the only one at the reunion that would know how to get in touch with me. She knew she could call Amy. So I clicked over and Erin told me that Scotty fell. Well at first I thought maybe he just tripped and fell down some stairs. Then Erin said, 'No, it's a lot more serious than that. There's head injuries. You should call the ambulance company and find out where he is.' And I think she gave me the phone number 'cause I don't remember lookin' it up. So I called and they told me he had been stat-flighted to Vanderbilt. So at that point I hung up. I was shakin' and I called my mom back and said, 'Don't go to church, somethin' bad has happened to Scotty.'"

I asked, "No one called your mom?"

"Nobody knew how to get ahold of her," she said. "His cellphone was in his man purse, as he called it, and my mom's number was in there, but the bag was gone and nobody knew how to call anybody. Thank God for Erin Gibson!"

"And he didn't have a license," I added, "so whoever found him didn't know who he was, right?"

"Right. He did have a nametag on from the reunion that said 'Jeremy,' his first name." She quickly changed direction. "Did Holli tell you about the phone call?"

"I've read something about it," I replied.

Holli Combs was Scotty's roommate while he lived in Lexington. Since his death, she has been more than outspoken about the investigation. Many blogs and forums have been inundated with her rants about what she thinks occurred. I, myself, had attempted, many times before the meeting with Brandi, to speak with Holli. As I would later come to find out, both on my own as well as through Brandi's comments, Holli was not the most accessible person in the world. She seemed to be operating on her own, *unusual*, for lack of a better word, terms. For every text message or email I would send her, I would receive twice as many in return, albeit weeks later and completely unrelated.

During one of her fierce online protests, Holli wrote about a call that came from Scotty's cellphone the morning his body was found. According to her statements, someone had used his cell to place a call, and she had obtained a recording of what was said. She was certain this would provide police with information about his mysterious injuries. She was also the first to report about a strange member profile found on a gay chat website after Scotty's death. I gathered from my conversation with Brandi that Holli's staunch advocate ways produced more bark than bite.

"I want to back up for a minute," I suggested. "Was the reunion in the Lodge or at the cabins?"

Brandi explained that the reunion itself was held in a party room in the Lodge, but three cabins were rented for reunion-goers who wanted to stay afterwards.

"I made a video of the last place he was seen at four o'clock in the morning using the phone. If you walk out the front door of the Lodge, you have to go all the way around to the back where he was found, and it's a huge circle to get back there. It's not just off to the side," she explained. "I've often thought if he was waitin' outside the Lodge for a cab to pick him up, maybe he was lured around the back. But it's a lot further around than I originally thought."

I felt like we were veering off track and I needed more clarification.

"So wait," I suggested, "he used the phone at four in the morning?" I was confused and had never heard this part of the story until now.

"They actually have phone records. Kentucky State Police found out that at 4:00 a.m. Scotty went to the front lobby and asked for a phonebook. They said he needed to call a cab. Which, to me, is a red flag. I was comin' at 8:00 a.m.; why would he...something was so wrong that he would leave at four in the mornin'?" She continued to remark, "Scotty was a rational person. It wasn't like he thought, 'I'm tired of this place, I'm gonna pay $80 to go home.' He didn't have a lot of money. He worked and saved every penny he had. "

"Did a cab show up?" I inquired.

"I don't know if it was ever confirmed or not. Maybe he just called to see how much a cab ride was gonna be. But the person at the front desk said they gave him a phonebook. Said he was coherent, very friendly, walked straight, didn't seem drunk. That was somethin' everybody thought...that he was drunk and fell off the wall. But the police traced the phone call back to the cab company. If he was waitin' for a cab then why did he go around back?" Brandi was both describing to me her theories as well as formulating more while she spoke. "If he knew a cab was coming, maybe he went to the cabins to tell everybody he was leaving. The only people awake that late were him and the four guys, according to police. Everyone else was suspected of being asleep. And the four guys who were awake, he didn't like, so I don't think he would have thought to go tell Bryant goodbye, you know? He was one of 'em that made fun of Scotty in high school for being gay, so why go tell him goodbye?"

She started to describe another scenario.

"Maybe," she said, "he figured the cab ride was too much money and he decided to stay and see if he could get back into the cabins and started to walk back down there. It seems I recall from the state trooper that he was waitin' for the cab, the cab came, but because no one was out there, the cab left."

"Did anybody see the cab?" I asked.

"No. Well I don't know. That's all information they got from the cab company I think," she said.

"So what all was left behind? His messenger bag?"

"Yeah. I went back to the State Park the next day. I was still a mess. I met with two people; a man and a woman, and told them I had come to pick up Scotty's belongings. They said, 'I'm sorry but we can't give this to you.' Well I was in hysterics! I was yelling, 'You have to give me his stuff! I need his apartment keys. I have to go turn things off. I need to make sure he didn't leave a candle burning!" She laughed at her own silly idea. "I said, 'I need his cellphone. My brother's in a coma. Nobody knows. I need to get in touch with people in his phone.' So they felt kinda bad for me and made a copy of everything in his wallet and gave it to me. His wallet was soaked, because from around 4:00 a.m. when they saw him last to around 8:00 a.m., it poured rain."

"What about his clothes," I asked. "Were any clothes left behind?"

"The stat-flight took off with his clothes. His clothes and his glasses, we never saw again. The strange thing is that his glasses were totally unscratched. And they were found about five feet away from him. He was legally blind without his glasses. And they fit him so tight. I even made the comment about how his skin protruded on each side of 'em. He always wore his glasses. They fit him snug, but we never saw 'em again."

I noted *glasses*.

"And his clothes?" I asked.

"I may have had his clothes at some point. The rangers at the Park gave me a box of stuff with biohazard tape all over it. It sat in my closet for weeks and I was terrified to open it. The bloody clothes just freaked me out too much," she said.

"But you got his wallet?"

"Yeah, and everything in it. He had about $80 in soaking wet twenty dollar bills. There was a Western Kentucky ID, where he had gone to school. He didn't have a license. His insurance card. I gave it all to my mom and she put it in a Ziplock bag. I don't know what she did with it," she continued. "Then I asked to speak to one of the rangers. You know, the State Park was still handlin' the investigation at this point. They had never done anything like this before, but for some reason they felt like they were trained enough to handle a possible homicide. I don't know what they were thinkin'. They asked me if I wanted to meet Veachell Adwell, and I did."

I had to clarify, "He was the ranger on the scene?"

"Yeah. I asked him where all of Scotty's things were and he told me he had them in a box in the back of his cruiser. I told him I wanted it, and he said he couldn't give it to me but he'd let me go through it," she said.

"And leave fingerprints all over everything," I joked.

She smiled. "Actually he put on gloves and showed everything to me. Everything in the box was soakin' wet: CDs, bubblegum, Chapstick, cellphone. So I said, 'I want the phone,' and he told me he couldn't give it to me. So I started screamin', 'My brother's in a coma, nobody knows, he has friends I have to call and tell!' I said I'd stand right there and make the calls then give the phone back to him. Then he said, 'Well I don't really see what the phone has to do with anything,' so he let me have it!"

I had heard about the carelessness of the rangers in their investigation and here was a prime example. I was stunned.

"The police could have gotten phone records through the phone company, so it wasn't that big of a deal, but he really shouldn't have let me have the phone. But I'm thankful he did 'cause that's how I got ahold of all his friends to let them know what had happened."

I interrupted, "When you got the phone, did you think to see who the last call was that he dialed?"

"I hit the 'Call' button first to see who he had called last, and it said 'Holli.' Then I looked at the time of the call and it said 7:44 a.m., and I thought that wasn't possible. They found him at 7:00 a.m. unconscious, and then he was flown to Vanderbilt. Well I started to freak out, so I called Holli and left a message, but didn't tell her why I was callin'. She called me back later, I told her what had happened, and she immediately drove to Nashville, got a room at the Hilton, stayed the whole time he was there. She never went home. But while we were at the hospital she told me that Scotty had called her at 7:44 a.m. and I said, 'I know. I meant to say somethin' to you about that.' And she said, 'But it wasn't Scotty.' She told me that it was a lot of background noise, radio static, and somebody yelling 'Jeremy, Jeremy!'"

I was confused and curious. "So what is it? How did that call get made?"

"I can only assume that, while they were taking off his man purse, one of the numbers got hit and dialed her by accident. I think it was strange that it was Holli who got called. Not strange," she clarified, "ironic."

"How long was he in the hospital?" I asked.

"Eleven days. In a coma the entire time."

"What were the injuries?"

She sighed again. "He had...and if you're not successful gettin' the medical records, I might be able to get my mom to cooperate..."

I interrupted once more. "Actually, I have it here." I dug through my own man purse and pulled out the copy of the records from the medical examiner.

"His death certificate says he fell from a boat dock," she told me.

"That was a question I had for you," I replied. "Here it mentions he fell from a barge in Bowling Green." I pointed out the phrase in the report while she read aloud.

"*Being held on a barge. He fell overboard approximately thirty feet,*" she read.

"Have you seen that before?" I asked.

"No."

I pointed to a name on the report. "Do you know who this is? Sherrie Saint?"

"No," she said flatly.

I could tell Brandi was confused by this report that contained misinformation. She spoke to me about the explanation she had heard from Dr. Bruce Levy, the medical examiner that reported Scotty's autopsy.

"What they tried to say," she began, "was that when he fell, he landed on his head, which took all the force. I'm tellin' you, he didn't have a contusion on his head, he didn't have a cut, he didn't have a fractured skull. Six foot something, 200 pounds, fallin' eleven feet. They said he lost his footing. If you lose your footing you're gonna try to catch yourself. I've seen the loading dock where he supposedly fell. I've measured it. It's exactly eleven feet. They say he lost his footing and landed on his head and suffered brain injuries. But he had no scratches on him. I think there was one little bruise on his elbow. There's no cuts, no bruises, no scratches, no broken bones. And to fall from that, especially if they first said thirty feet, wouldn't you have a broken bone?"

"What about his neck?" I asked.

"Nope, not a broken neck. He was perfectly intact. They said the reason why the head trauma was so bad was because his head took the entire blow, and since it didn't crack his skull there was more damage inside the skull with swelling. I don't think the blow to his head is what killed him. He laid there for four hours with all that swelling. Four hours is a long time to lay with a head injury. If he'd gotten immediate medical attention, the swelling wouldn't have been so severe. They were trying to portray that his head took the entire force and that's why it was so bad. It was so bad because he lay there for so long."

Brandi continued to thumb through the report, but kept going back to the paragraph written by Sherrie Saint.

"*Fell overboard,*" she re-read. "*Being held on a barge. Thirty feet.* All of this is wrong. Who wrote this?"

"She was one of the examiners apparently," I told her. I went on to point out another statement written by Dr. Levy. "He wrote that the injuries came '*from a moving head striking a non-moving object.*' The doctor feels that his head hit something ,as opposed to something hitting his head."

Brandi continued to read the description of Scotty's injuries. "'*Enlargement of liver and spleen...bleeding between the skull and scalp...bruise on crown of head.*' Okay, so he did have a bruise." She looked up at me and said sarcastically, "Well I guess if you fall thirty feet, you're gonna have a bruise!"

"It mentions a scar on his chest," I said. "Was that new or a previous injury?"

"He had a bike wreck when he was kid...ironically with a concrete block." She read some more. "'*Teeth in good repair.*' He had perfect teeth, beautiful teeth. The corner of one of his teeth was chipped slightly from this. It wasn't like that before."

Apparently she caught something in the report that didn't seem right. "*Laceration,*" she read. "We were told there were no lacerations on his head; that it was all internal. They told us when his head hit, his brain was thrown forwards and backwards and it just bruised severely on the front and back. '*Scalp and skull are unremarkable*' it says. So there was *no* mark on his head. Other than a bruise. A bruise isn't a mark?!" She was getting frustrated with the apparent discrepancies. Then she suddenly asked me something I wasn't expecting.

"I know you're writin' about all this, but are your intentions to reopen this case as part of your book?"

"I, uh, uh," I fumbled with my words. "I don't want to...no, I'm not interested in reopening the case. Honestly, from my standpoint, I'm allowed access to public records so long as the case is closed. I don't want to jeopardize that," I said selfishly.

Brandi then suggested something I hadn't thought of before she asked. "My question to you, I guess, is would you like to have everything you need and then the case be reopened? Then you hold off on your book until it's done so you can have a great ending?"

I admired her hopefulness and agreed. "Sure," I said. Later, after having time to reflect about what I had just offered, I would second-guess my decision. I wasn't sure I could wait that long to complete my story, but time would prove an important role in bringing about interesting results.

"Because I have a friend of a friend," she started to tell me, "who's a medical examiner in Louisville. He's also a part-time deputy coroner in Richardsville, so he knows people. I asked him about all this, and he said, from the minute he heard about Scotty's case, he never forgot it. Said it didn't make sense to him either. He told me he'd review the medical records. I mean, they're not gonna exhume the body or anything, just give an opinion. Because even with an affidavit from this guy, it's conflicting with what they said originally. I feel like that would be reason enough to reopen it."

I could see Brandi was getting caught up in the moment. She was reading statements that she felt weren't true, and now with me on her side to help bring this case back to light, she was overwhelmed with hope. I was just wishing it wasn't false hope, so I changed the subject again. "Were police updating you about what was going on?"

"Oh yeah," she said. "Detective West, the lead investigator, was very cooperative and said to call him whenever. My dad was overzealous and called him all the time. We had a lot of respect for him. He seemed to be doin' a good job. And he was quoted as sayin' he felt like he had walked into a mess from the Park's Department. I'm sure you read that."

I nodded. Detective West had made the comment to a reporter from *The Louisville Courier-Journal* saying, "*I think they realized, 'Hey this is above our heads. But our position is sometimes we get in a no-win position where, if we adopt it, we inherit a case that is tainted from the beginning. It's really a no-win for us.*"

Brandi continued, "But it was Karen Davis who was totally absent from the whole thing,"

"What was her role," I asked.

"She's the Commonwealth Attorney. Her job is to represent the victim, so she was supposed to be our prosecutor--our unhired attorney, if you will. She was legally responsible to represent us on behalf of somethin' that happened in her jurisdiction. But she was not there for anything!" Brandi expressed a scowl across her face. I could tell the subject of Karen Davis was a sore one. "She didn't call us, she never returned phone calls. She was the most *impossible* person to reach at all times."

Another note. *Interview Karen Davis.*

"We had that box with all the biohazard tape on it. I kept calling Karen Davis's office day after day and leavin' messages for her. 'I have to talk to Karen. I have this box of evidence that needs to be forensically tested for fibers, hair, whatever. Isn't there anything you can do?' I finally got a hold of her one day and she said, 'I'm leavin' the office right now. Call me back next week.' Well I carried that box in my trunk forever and kept calling her, but nothin'. Then I got in touch with her and told her somebody needs to do something with that box, and she told me to bring it by and drop it off, and I did. I don't even think I saw her the day I dropped it off. I don't know who ended up with it?"

"You said that the box came from the Parks' Department. Did Kentucky State Police ever have it?"

Brandi explained, "KSP was working for Karen. I spoke to Detective West and told him I had that box. He told me I had to give it to her first. She was impossible. One day it came out in *The Daily Times*, 'Commonwealth to Present Martin Case to Grand Jury on Thursday.'" Brandi gestured the headline in the air, accentuating each word. "My family and I were stunned. She was supposed to keep us informed. Well we're freakin' out, callin' her. She said it wasn't true and she didn't know where the *Daily Times* got that information. She said, 'I guarantee it's not goin' to the Grand Jury on Thursday 'cause I haven't even looked at the file.' Well that right there sent me into a fury! She hadn't even looked at it! This was months into the investigation!"

Brandi's face was getting slightly red. She took a deep breath and continued talking.

"I was furious that she hadn't even looked at the file, but I knew that Detective West was working on it and thought maybe she didn't have to do anything but sit there and do nothing until somebody else does somethin'."

I was curious to find out why the local newspaper had printed the story about a Grand Jury that wasn't scheduled to meet. I just happened to have copies of every article from the *Daily Times* pertaining to Scotty, which Brandi and I sorted through.

She began reading one. "'…*which included Martin being pushed or chased off a ledge, falling accidentally or a third scenario where Martin had been injured and moved to another location and left by the Lodge.*' I don't believe the wall had anything to do with it," she confessed. "And I don't feel like he was injured at another location and moved. The state police came to Vanderbilt. They tried to dig blood out from under his fingernails, but by the time they got there he had been bathed five or six times. Plus, he was such a nail biter. He bit his nails down to the quick."

I thought Brandi had gotten off track about Karen, but she started up again. "There's a couple of things that really bother me about all this. Detective West. If I give you a job to do and you do it, but it's not successful, it probably won't get you a huge promotion. He got one."

I learned that Sergeant West was promoted to Lieutenant and moved to Pikeville, Kentucky after the Grand Jury met.

"I've always felt like," Brandi began again, "Karen Davis didn't want this case to be solved. She had an election comin' up. The four suspects are a judge's nephew, a doctor's son, a city council woman's son, and a realtor's son. How much pull do they have in this town? They probably have enough power to get her re-elected. Not to mention that I heard rumors that she's friends with some of 'em. I don't even know the word to describe her. Well I do, but I'm trying to be nice." She smiled. "She's a…follower, she's not a leader. How many murders have happened in Barren County that are unsolved since she's been in office? Do you know about 'em?"

I shook my head, although I had read a recent account of a wife who shot her husband and Karen Davis had somehow managed to have the charges dropped.

"There's a lot of things unsolved around here, and sometimes I just don't think she's very good at her job. She sure didn't do anything on our behalf and this case. She's very...distant," she said. "You know she was appointed to that position by Judge Patton when he left to be Chief Circuit Judge. She wasn't voted in to start with! People joke around here that it's no longer Barren County, but Karen County."

I asked, "Did the family ever meet directly with her?"

"No. Never met her. My mom couldn't pick her out of a crowd."

I thought this incredibly odd, and I was starting to dislike the woman, even though my position was to remain impartial.

Brandi said, "When she campaigned to get re-elected, which I don't think is the right word since she wasn't elected to begin with, I was very vocal on *The Daily Times*'s website about her. I have a big problem with the fact that we weren't even consoled, never offered counselin'. She didn't care. She was supposed to represent our family for my brother, who's the victim. I feel like she did nothin'. I know she did nothin'. It was obvious she did nothin'. The only time we ever met her was the day we went to the Grand Jury, and she was very cold to us."

"She said she had presented everything to the jury, and I said, 'What exactly did you present?' Because there's reasonable doubt. The jury should have enough common sense. There's people who said these four guys were pickin' on him, guys who he wouldn't have been friends with in high school. There's the jocks and there's the drum major of the band. They stood on the third floor of Glasgow High School and called him a fag every time he walked by. And he's hangin' out with them in their cabin?! And he ends up dead?! Reasonable doubt comes to my mind. But I don't know what she told 'em. I'd love to have minutes from that Grand Jury, but I think you have to go through her to get 'em."

At this point, I thought, my work was cut out for me. I jotted down *Grand Jury Minutes*.

"It was so disappointing," Brandi said. I couldn't tell if she was telling me or reminding herself. "Karen explained to us that she told the jury everything from beginning to end and they didn't see that there was enough evidence to indict anybody. It was just...so disappointing," she repeated. "And we never heard from her again."

"Were you doing any investigating on your own," I asked her.

"No. I trusted that KSP knew what they were doin'. West kept in touch with me. If I asked him somethin', he'd tell me. He told me things like, there was a piece of gum found near Scotty. Could have been anybody's, but was it picked up and tested for saliva from any of the four guys? No."

"Talk about that," I asked. "The four guys who were last seen with him. How do you know those were the four guys?"

"Sergeant West told me. That's where I got my information. And Michelle Huffman. She's our cousin. She was there that night. Have you talked to her?" she asked me.

"I haven't, but I plan to," I explained.

"I've already talked to her about you. She said she would be willing to speak with you, too. A lot of the reunion-goers all mentioned the same four guys."

I was confused. "Mentioned them how?" I asked.

"As in that Scotty went into their cabin. Some mentioned that they were pickin' on him earlier in the night. What other reason would they have to pick on him? I mean, they're cocky jocks from rich families. And here's Scotty, just average guy, dancin' with Taylor Bale and Anne Gentry, beautiful, rich girls that loved Scotty dearly, you know. Have you talked to Anne Gentry?"

"No, I haven't."

Brandi looked sad when she started to speak. "Please talk to Anne Gentry, because I haven't. I'm confident that there's a reason why I haven't seen or heard from her. She and Scotty were very close. She's the one person I was devastated didn't come to the funeral. Her family sent flowers, but she didn't show up and she didn't live that far away. I mean, Owen Price came, and he lives in Key West."

I found out that Scotty and Owen were close friends in high school; both were in the band.

"And Owen's mom was awesome," Brandi said. "She was really there for us because she said 'I know why they did it, and it could have been my son." And Wyatt Wilson's mom said the same thing. You know, somebody with a straight child wouldn't have said that. We got a lot of support that way from people who could understand."

Brandi looked reflective. "But Anne," she started again, "I don't know. She never showed up, she didn't call, nothing. Nothing. You know, her mom is president of the bank, and her family is close with those other families. Maybe she felt a moral dilemma because she was close to Scotty, but her parents are close to those other parents. She's the one person I can't get over not being there."

The time had finally come for me to ask the big question. "You've mentioned the four. Who are the four? Let's name the four just so I know."

Without hesitation Brandi answered calmly, "John Dickenson, Blake Oliver, Chris York, and Bryant Vincent." She read off the names like she had rehearsed this many time before.

"I wish Michelle could meet us here and bring the photo," Brandi said. "Did you hear about the photo?"

I was aware of no photo and not sure what Brandi was speaking about. "No," I said.

"At the reunion," she began, "Michelle took a picture of all the girls together and all the guys together. In the photo with the guys are two interesting things. The first thing you notice is the angel that's circled around Blake Oliver."

"An angel?" I asked. I had definitely never heard this story before.

Brandi continued, "She's reprinted it a hundred times and it still comes out. I don't have a copy of it, but I think my mom does. It looks like a head and a set of wings, and it goes all around Blake Oliver's body. It's the strangest thing you've ever seen. It freaked me out for weeks."

I was freaking out myself. "I'm getting chills just thinking about it.

Oh my God!" I exclaimed.

"The other thing you notice is that Bryant is standing by Scotty making a gay gesture. Now when I say 'gay gesture,' it could have been a straight gesture, but comin' from Bryant Vincent, I feel like it's directed towards Scotty," she said.

"And I'm not sayin' Bryant did it, but if one person is responsible for his injuries, the other three know about it, so to me," she continued, "they're all responsible. I suggested to KSP at some point to subpoena their phone records. I guarantee they're callin' each other a hundred times to get their stories straight."

"What did the police say about that?" I asked.

"West said 'We don't have to subpoena 'em, they've all admitted it. They've all admitted that since it happened they have all been callin' each other.' Well why do they care? They never cared about him before. If they cared enough to talk about it to each other, why weren't they callin' and checkin' in on him? Bryant Vincent doesn't care. I heard somethin' peculiar from Michelle about him too. He's a football coach livin' in Troy, Alabama. He was in town stayin' with his mother for the Memorial Day weekend, for his reunion, whatever. Obviously, Memorial Day, he doesn't have to go back to work until Tuesday. It's a long weekend and he was scheduled to stay with his mom for the weekend. From what I understand, he hauled ass back to Alabama Sunday morning. Left abruptly. A lot of people left that mornin' before anybody came. The Park didn't contain 'em."

"So no one was being interviewed by the Park's officials that morning?" I asked.

"Whoever was left," she said. "But they let so many people leave…and that's where the KSP said there was such a big mess because the people who left, they had to track down and interview. Had they been able to get them right then, it would have been a lot better."

"Do you know anybody who was interviewed that morning?"

Brandi shook her head. "No, but that should all be in the report. I was told that the report contained the full interviews of everybody."

"Was Michelle interviewed," I asked.

"She didn't spend the night, but she was interviewed extensively, because she was one of the closest to him. At some point I didn't really care what everybody said, I wanted to know what Bryant and all of 'em said. I know that Bryant took a lie detector test and it was inconclusive."

"Did West tell you that?"

She answered, "Yes, said he was the only one of the four who voluntarily took it, and it was inconclusive. The others refused and hired attorneys. Local attorneys."

Another note. *Lie detector test. Inconclusive.* I was getting restless. I wanted those reports from KSP now. There was so much I had to find out.

I started to change gears again. "In one of Holli's posts online she mentioned something about the chat site, Gay.com. What can you tell me about that?" I asked.

"All I know..., " she began. I could tell this was going to be a long and detailed story. "All I know is that after Scotty died we went to his apartment. I took all his furniture, because we didn't want to get rid of it or sell it. I got rid of what I had and put his stuff in my house. I also took his computer. Now, when I hooked it up at home, I clicked on the dropdown box and it showed the last website, which was Gay.com. Well I didn't know passwords or anything so I couldn't get on there. And I didn't think anything about it. I just assumed he used it chat with people online when he was living in Bowling Green."

"A way of meeting people," I said.

"Right. Well that computer has been in my way for three and a half years, to be honest with you. It's just a big, old clunky computer, and I used it for a while. Then I got a new Dell and started having problems with it, so I dragged Scotty's back out of the closet one day. For some reason, I just never got rid of it. And I've thought about having it forensically backed up."

"What do you mean?" I asked.

"When I worked at the Justice Center, there were two detectives that came there, and I talked to them about backing up a computer. They said you could have the entire history of the computer stored on CDs and then go through them to see what all was on there. They said some companies would give you a certificate of authenticity to state that they did it, and you didn't doctor the documents. But they told me that any such computer should be turned over to KSP. Well I thought, they're gonna have a field day with the Gay.com and whatever. And if there's nothing on there, it's none of their business. I'd rather do it myself and see if there's a reason to let KSP have it."

"Of course," I agreed.

"So one day Holli and I were talkin', and she mentioned to me that somebody got on Gay.com after Scotty died and was posing as him; had posts and a profile."

"How did she know that?"

"She said some friends of hers had known about it for a long time, but didn't tell her right away 'cause they knew it would upset her. She said the person posted his picture, said 'Hey, come meet me,' sendin' messages to people. Said this person was actin' erratically on there, and so her friends started sending messages sayin', 'Why are you doin' this?' and the person wrote back and said something about murder, which threw off red flags. I don't know if it said, '*Oh, he was murdered*,' you know. But it was somebody usin' his picture on there almost like revenge."

"Interesting," I thought aloud.

"When she told me that, I started havin' thoughts, one after another, and I may have just convinced myself, but there's Blake Oliver who lives in Lexington. He lived there when Scotty lived there. He's never had a girlfriend that anybody can remember. And I started hearin' rumors. I heard that the other guys caught Scotty with Blake. And I thought, no they didn't. Blake Oliver is straight. Plus, Scotty ain't interested in Blake Oliver. He's not into straight people. And I mentioned it to Michelle, and she had heard that it was Bryant Vincent that got caught with him. Well Bryant's wife was there, and they have children, so I have a hard time believing that."

I didn't say anything at this point, but knew all too well that, just because a guy is married with children, doesn't mean he won't taste the forbidden fruit, so to speak. I didn't figure now was the best time to elaborate with Brandi.

"What did the guys say in their interviews? Do you know?" I asked.

"Sergeant West told me that the four guys all had the same story."

I interjected, "Of course they did."

"Exactly. Whatever happened to him at four in the mornin', they had until eight in the mornin' to come up with an alibi. Told me they all said, 'He came into our cabin and was hittin' on us. He was grabbin' us and doin' all kinds of stuff.' Well, he wasn't drunk, and I can't imagine him doin' that drunk or sober. It wasn't in his character. I never saw him hit on gay people, much less, straight people. He was such a private person that he wouldn't do that. I mean, he may jokingly do it with friends, but not four strangers who didn't like him."

"Did these four guys all share the same cabin?" I asked.

"Yeah, and so there was no logical explanation for him to be there to start with. I don't know if they invited him to come in. I can't imagine him takin' the invitation, which kinda makes me think there had to have been a reason why he went in there initially. Could it have been Blake? Then I started thinkin' about the Gay.com thing again. Maybe he met one of 'em online before the reunion, and that's why he wanted to go so bad."

My mind was now racing with my own theories. Friends who knew I was writing about this story had all agreed that it sounded unreal, like a movie. I was beginning to understand why. Brandi was bringing up points I had never heard, and it was fascinating. It didn't sound real to me, but there I was, sitting in front of her, and she was sharing what she knew to be true. I couldn't help but be intrigued.

"I don't know what to think about all that. I thought about Blake, then forgot about it until Michelle showed me the photo of the angel of death or whatever, wrapped around his picture. I just…don't know."

"Are there any other fishy details that we haven't discussed?" I asked. I was hoping Brandi would bring up another unexplained angle like the

Gay.com profile or the angel in the photo. Her answer surprised me.

"Well there's one thing I hate to even talk about. If you don't already know, I'm sure you'll read about it in the report," she said. "Do you know about the meth?"

Meth.

"No," I said.

"Scotty's injuries were so severe; he got hooked up to machines and pain medicine right away. There were no toxicology reports, so there's no way to prove that he had done any drugs or had any alcohol. All we know is the last person who saw him in the lobby of the Lodge said he was very polite, very coherent, seemed to walk straight, talk fine, you know. But when the Park Ranger was shuffling through his bag, showing me things, he pulled out a little jewelry box and said, 'What's this?'"

At that moment, Brandi's cellphone began to ring, and I let her know it was fine if she needed to answer it. She looked at the incoming number, silenced the call, and set the phone back on the table. I was glad because I wanted to know more about the little jewelry box.

"So Ranger Adwell opens the box, lifts up the bottom part, and there was a little bag of white stuff," she said. "He says to me, 'Well we didn't see this before when we went through here,' which I just thought was insane. More red flags were going off that told me nobody knew what they were doin'. He asked me if I thought the box was Scotty's, and I told him I didn't know. I didn't know. I know it's something that he had done before, but not on a regular basis. But it could've been given to him that night. No one else was tested for drugs, and there was no way to prove who it belonged to."

I was stunned. I never would have pictured Scotty as a meth user, but the last time we had seen each other was in college. A lot can change in seven years. My prepared questions had come to an end, but I had to know one thing.

"So what do you think really happened?" I asked.

Brandi sighed once more and stared at me for a few seconds before answering. "I have always thought it was just a shove. I have never thought that anybody intentionally killed him or hurt him with intent to kill him. Something happened in that cabin, whether it was getting caught with somebody and they were humiliated, so they chased after him. Maybe that's when he called the cab 'cause he knew they were after him and he had to get the heck outta there. I mean, I know for sure something happened for him to leave right then. He would not have irrationally gotten a cab and left for no reason. But then again, something happened after the call to the cab company that caused him to stay. I just feel like it was a shove that caused him to lose his balance and fall back. Maybe if someone pushed him down they thought he'd just wake up, so they didn't bother to check on him."

"Was there blood on the concrete?" I asked.

"I don't know if his head was resting on a cinderblock or if it was on the ground, but they said he was layin' in a pool of blood."

I had a theory I wanted to pass by her, one I had thought of after reading the medical examiner's report.

"Could he have already been down in the alleyway and struck on the back of the head with an object that caused him to fall down," I asked. Dr. Levy had written in the report that his moving head struck a non-moving object. I am no forensic investigator, and most of my detective work comes from *CSI*, but I had wondered if someone had lured Scotty down the incline of the loading dock. I knew it was dark down there, and if someone had the intention to cause harm, that's a pretty good place to do it. It's also a surreptitious place for two people to make out.

"There's another theory," she began, "that someone dragged him to the location he was found. Police never checked the bottom of his shoes. They never checked for footprints, they didn't check for drag marks in the mud. It rained. The ground would have been softer and made deeper marks, but no one thought to check any of this." I could see that Brandi was getting riled up again. I made yet another note. *Shoes*.

"It really pissed me off!" she said. "They didn't check that piece of gum. As small as it was, they should have checked it. They didn't check his clothes. They had the Highland Games comin' up the following weekend.

One day there's yellow tape around the Lodge, the next day it's gone. They obviously didn't want to draw attention to this because people ain't gonna come from all over the world to a murder scene! If I just knew what happened! Justice will come one way or another but peace has got to come at some point."

Brandi was looking fatigued and I expected our meeting may be dragging on for her, but I was reminded that she loved talking about Scotty. I think the years since his death were weighing on her, and I felt it best to wrap it up.

"Thank you so much for meeting with me. It's so reassuring that you approve of what I'm doing. I know what a personal matter it is to you and your family, and after today I don't feel like I'm treading where I shouldn't."

Brandi nodded. "And my mom doesn't want to relive it. She didn't want his personal life public. I told her it was no secret that Scotty was gay and if someone wrote about, it's not a lie. Scotty would have told you himself. It's funny though, a lot of people didn't know until it happened. And there's a lot of people who still don't know."

She looked directly at me. "Hate crime," she said. "Those words never came about. It was never portrayed as a hate crime."

"Should it have been? Would it have made a difference?" I asked.

"I don't think it would, but I think it would have gotten more attention. But in this town, you can't use those words too freely. That's still something not acceptable here 'cause we're in the Bible Belt," she said. "There's a lot of gay people in Glasgow, and the majority of 'em leave for that reason. I don't know if it would have made a difference."

I was beginning to tire myself, though I was finding it all so fascinating. The time had finally come to depart. I thanked Brandi once again and told her I would keep in touch. Before we separated I had one final question to ask, and I was glad I did.

"Have you ever run into any of the four guys?" I inquired.

"No, but if I ever do, you'll hear about it," she said. "I would hope I would be a Christian, but I'm afraid I would just be a Martin!"

Three

After leaving the interview with Brandi, I headed towards my mom's house. We were scheduled to have dinner, but about half way there I decided instead to turn around and pay a quick visit to the Lodge. I was already late, so a few more minutes wouldn't hurt. It's common knowledge in Glasgow that you can get anywhere in town within five minutes, and a drive to the Lodge only adds another ten.

The drive out, along Scottsville Road, is actually pretty serene. It was a pleasant distraction from the jumble of frenzied information I had just consumed, thanks to Brandi. I was able to take a few moments to breathe and set aside the frustration I felt once our meeting was over.

The vast majority of scenery is farmland, but every so often I was reminded of something from my past. A boarded-up building on my right used to be the Colonial House Restaurant, a Sunday afternoon lunch spot that my family would visit after church. Most Sundays were spent on my grandparent's farm with the chores of feeding the family placed upon my grandmother, but every so often we would meet them instead at Colonial House where its famous buffet was filled with every possible red meat, starch, and artery-fattening food you can imagine. Green beans cooked in bacon fat, mashed potatoes creamed with pounds of butter, and every poor animal deep-fried, resting under red hot lamps for the taking.

Passing another eatery up ahead, and one that I'm surprised to see still standing, is Bully's Restaurant. There isn't anyone in these parts who doesn't know about Bully's famous catfish. Had I not had dinner plans back at my mom's house, I could have easily been tempted to turn the car directly into Bully's parking lot. But I forged on.

At Browning School Road stands a sign for the first Houchens grocery. Houchens is a supermarket chain in the region and the little shed that started it all sits atop a long, winding hill alongside my route. Ages ago the company would host family festivals and picnics for the employees and their families. Since my dad was once a manager of one of the stores we would sometimes visit the recreational park in the summertime and partake of the potlucks.

Another side road in the distance would lead to a small lake house once owned by Susannah's father. In high school a bunch of us would hang out there, and although I recall spending numerous times there, I have forgotten all but two specific details about the place. The only time I can vividly remember staying there is a night during high school when four of us "borrowed" a friend's car while she slept and drove an hour away to the Waffle House in Elizabethtown to chow down at two o'clock in the morning. My second memory about the lake house is that I used it as an excuse during the summer after graduation when lying to my mom, telling her I was spending the night there, when in fact, I was spending the night with my first boyfriend in Bowling Green. This stretch of road was quickly becoming my Memory Lane.

In the distance I noticed something I had never seen before. A large sign was planted in a field off to my right. Above it, the sky was growing dark. As I approached, I noticed it read, "Jesus said you be ashamed of me and I will be ashamed of you." I was ashamed of the person who had posted the sign here.

A loud clap of thunder came barreling on top of me, and suddenly the car was drenched with rain. Unable to see ahead, I quickly turned on my wipers and headlights, then pulled over to the side of the road in an attempt to wait out the torrential downpour. From the side window I soon noticed I was sitting directly to the left of the menacing billboard. We stared at one another until the rain slacked up and I had eventually decided to save my park visit for another day and head back to the house.

As I entered my bedroom and turned on the light I noticed a strategically placed magazine on my pillow. I picked it up. The photo on the cover showed a quaint, little town nestled below two rolling hills in the background. The leaves on the trees were brightly colored in autumnal hues, and a lazy river moved motionless in the foreground. *The Progressive Farmer*, I read aloud, questioning the magazine's title.

In large font, spread about the river itself, it read, "Best Places To Live In Rural America."

"Page fifteen," a voice startled me from behind. My mom was standing in the doorway with a smirk on her face.

"What is this?" I asked her.

"Page fifteen," she repeated.

I thumbed the pages to find a green pasture, complete with red barn and grain silo, starting back at me, accompanied by a surprising headline.

I was dumbfounded by what I read. "Barren County is the best place to live in rural America?!"

"According to *Progressive Farmer* magazine," my mom clarified.

I began to read the article. *"It's the kind of place where people come, like what they see, then decide to call it home."*

"Who are these people?" I asked bitterly. Raised eyebrows were my mother's only response. I continued reading. *"With its rolling farmland and friendly residents, there's little reason to wonder why."* I had to laugh. Even Joe Link, the executive editor of the magazine, made a comment about his impression of the county. "Everybody knows everybody and it seems to have a really good community spirit," he said.

I looked at my mom with vacant eyes. "I just don't know what to say? Why didn't you tell me about this earlier?"

"It must have slipped my mind," she said. "But everybody in town is talkin' about it. You'd think we'd made the cover of *Life* the way everyone keeps carryin' on."

I tossed the magazine back on the bed. "I challenge you to find five people in this county who subscribed to *Progressive Farmer* before this article came out. I'm sorry to laugh, but this is hilarious," I said.

"There's more," my mom continued.

I closed my eyes and placed my head in my hands. "Please don't tell me *Good Morning America* is going to be here."

My mother smiled. "Nope," she said, "The *Today* Show."

"WHHHAAAT?" I screamed. "YOU'RE KIDDING ME!"

"Go eat," she said, kissing me on the cheek. As she walked out of the room, she yelled back, "Your supper's getting cold."

I sat on the edge of the bed and picked up the magazine again. Who voted on this, I wondered, then shook my head. I stared at the cover once more before placing it under my arm and headed towards the dining room.

After dinner I decided to check my email and read some of the many comments posted on a local Glasgow blog. Occasionally I would check this site to see what was being written, if anything, about Scotty. I knew his friend, Holli, liked to keep his story out in cyberspace with the hopes, I felt, of entrapment. She feels that if she can stir the pot, maybe someone posting comments will divulge enough information to incriminate someone else. This particular forum contained such threads as "Impeach the President," "The Best Wal-Mart Employees," "Chickens For Sale," and "Ear Stapling for Weight Loss." I really wish I could make these up, but they are real.

I had previously bookmarked these pages and wanted to see if any had been updated. Most of the postings were either from Holli, herself, or from Brandi, responding to others' questions about the case; even notes of sympathy. Yet, sprinkled throughout the online conversation I saw postings stating that gays are "sick" and "you perverts are going to hell." One even read "go get AIDS." I was disgusted, but certainly not surprised.

Lots of comments made reference to the families of the boys and their connection to other local attorneys, judges, and "big wigs," as some referred. "Everybody knows who did it," one posted. "Who's doing the paying off? If you don't have money, then you don't have a hand in the legal system."

I never gave much thought to the idea that the accused boys' families played much of a role in the investigation, but after to speaking to Scotty's cousin, Michelle Huffman, I started to change my thinking.

"Glasgow is a who's-who town," she would tell me, "and the four names that were mentioned throughout all come from..." She paused. "Pillars of society or whatever you want to call it. The fact that it was all kept quiet and swept under the rug was not surprising to me."

"Why not?" I asked.

"Had the shoe been on the other foot, had it been Scotty or someone like Scotty from a lower class family that was involved in a crime against one of them," she said, stressing the word *them*, "it would not have been so hush-hush in my opinion."

Of course I had grown up here and I certainly knew family names that were more respected throughout the community; names going back generations. But I never sensed that any family in town had the kind of pull of a Mafioso. I grew up believing my hometown was quaint, old-fashioned and nostalgically attractive, albeit boring at times.

I was naïve to accept it as biased, vicious, and corrupt. But maybe it was, I thought, at one time. Or was I simply projecting my ideals on a place I wanted to be pure, for whatever reason. Surely this town hadn't changed so drastically in such a short amount of time.

"Oh, it has," my friend Jennifer would tell me later. She was the same age as I and her family had lived in Barren County for as far back as anyone could remember. "That place is full of right-wing hypocrites! Super religious, conservative, right-wing hypocrites!"

"Why do you say that?" I asked her.

"I moved back there for a little while to get my life back in order. Anyway, I started hanging out with a lot of these housewives with obnoxious kids and husbands who go to work and hardly ever come home. These women do nothing but gossip about each other and stab each other in the back. Oh they'll go to church with their families on Sunday, but the night before, those housewives have been out gettin' drunk and screwin' other men."

I started to laugh.

"I'm serious," she said, "They all hated me 'cause I was single and thought I was after their husbands." With raised eyebrows and a cocked head, Jennifer scowled, "No, thank you."

"How long did you live in Glasgow?" I asked.

She explained, "Long enough to know it had changed and I didn't want to be a part of it. I don't know what it is, but things are different there than they used to be when we were growin' up."

"Like what?" I wanted to know.

Jennifer was silent for several seconds before answering. "Like there's people out there who have this incredible need for power, who feel like it's owed to them. There are people who'll do anything or say anything to get their way, no matter at what cost to others."

I sat there intently, as she had certainly garnered my attention of this topic.

She continued. "Back when they were gonna vote to make the county wet or moist or whatever the hell you wanna call it, there were terribly nasty things written in the paper and online about how the county was gonna go to hell if they allowed liquor sales in Glasgow. Then there's the story of the jailer who was allegedly sexually assaulting female staff members. And then there's the two police officers buying prescription drugs without a prescription and threatening to kill anyone who told on them."

"What the hell is going on there?" I exclaimed.

"I know," Jennifer said, "It's a regular den of thieves."

"So what do you know about Karen Davis," I asked, hoping she would have some juicy story about the Commonwealth Attorney.

"I don't really know much at all about her," she replied.

I was disappointed.

"But I know someone who would know," Jennifer said. "Someone who worked for the city and pretty closely to Karen."

Now I was intrigued.

Upon my return from Glasgow I received an email from UPS that a package had been left at my front door. I knew this had to be what I had been anxiously awaiting for weeks now. I stopped everything I was doing and raced home to finally accept it. Of course, racing home in Chicago is not as quick as it sounds. From where I was downtown, racing took about an hour once I had finally gotten a train, transferred to a bus, then walked home the remaining distance.

Approaching my building, I could see two large, white envelopes at the foot of the entryway door. This time, I truly raced to retrieve them. On the front of both envelopes was the seal of Kentucky, which also appears on its flag. Adopted in 1792 the seal contains two men, historically thought to be Daniel Boone and statesman Henry Clay, facing one another and clasping hands. The outer ring of the seal is adorned with the words, "Commonwealth of Kentucky", and within the inner circle, surrounding the two men, is the state's motto, "United we stand, divided we fall." I caught myself reading those words aloud before entering the building and heading upstairs. It should also be noted that the original image for the seal depicted the two men in a full embrace. To quote Kory, "I'm not sayin', I'm just sayin'".

Still shocked by the weight of the two envelopes, I tossed them on the dining room table and quickly called Kory to tell him the good news. Not answering, I left a voicemail and headed back to the table where I immediately ripped open the official report.

Four

On the afternoon of Monday, May 31, 2004, Trooper B.J. Eaton informed Lieutenant Eric Wolford that Park Ranger Veachell Adwell had contacted him earlier that day about a possible assault case occurring at the Barren River State Park. A male subject with life threatening injuries had been found behind the Lodge, Adwell told Eaton. He said that rangers had collected evidence and interviewed several guests of the Park.

Eaton informed Wolford, the Investigation Commander, that he had tried explaining to Adwell that this was a far too serious case for a road trooper to investigate, but he would contact a post supervisor for advice. Wolford then called Adwell himself, saying Kentucky State Police would probably not take over the case but would provide assistance to their offices. He cited the failure of the rangers to locate and interview key suspects after they had been identified as such, as well as the time lapse of well over thirty hours until KSP was notified that rangers had already processed the scene and collected evidence.

The decision was officially reached not to take over the investigation by Captain Wayne Mayfield, Commander, Post 3. Adwell was told that KSP would provide assistance to the Park in the investigation by assigning Trooper John Holbrook, who was placed on special detail to assist rangers throughout the duration of the investigation. Holbrook was assigned to the case due to being one of the most senior officers with over twenty years service within the agency. He also had valuable experience in working a number of death investigations and assaults.

On Wednesday, June 2nd, Lt. Wolford was discussing case investigations with Sergeant Shannon West at Post 3 when he mentioned the incident at the State Park involving Scotty Martin. In further discussions of their decision not to take the lead, Sergeant West said that he agreed, "that the factors they noted posed significant challenges with regarding to KSP reaching objective conclusions in this or any investigation. The transfer of evidence, and other transient factors, related to objective conclusions in this investigation would significantly affect the solvability of the case."

The next day Trooper Holbrook began his duties by contacting Commonwealth Attorney Karen Davis, who would, in turn, prepare subpoenas for medical reports. He then headed to the Barren River State Park to begin assisting Ranger Adwell with the investigation. The first person Holbrook wanted to speak with was John Moss, the cook who initially found Scotty lying at the bottom of the loading dock.

Moss said that at approximately 7:00 a.m. on Sunday morning he walked outside the kitchen for a smoke break. He left the rear loading dock to get a cigarette lighter from his car, and as he walked by the ramp, he noticed a man lying on the ground. He said he thought the man might have been drunk and sleeping it off, but upon seeing the blood, he went inside, called 911, and returned to the stranger until medical personnel arrived.

"I saw his head against the cinder block," Moss said, "and a pool of blood under and behind his head." He went on to describe Scotty's position. "He was lying on his right side with his left arm over his eyes. He had a black fanny pack-type bag in his left hand; the same hand on his face and eyes."

"I told him not to move," he said, "that help is on the way. While I was waiting, two guests approached. A man and woman. They recognized him as Scotty Thomas or Thompson, something like that," he told Holbrook. "I also heard the woman say it was all her fault and it shouldn't have happened."

After talking to John Moss, Trooper Holbrook walked towards the loading dock to view the scene for himself. Ranger R.J. Hogue had marked off the area with yellow police tape. Five days had passed since Scotty was discovered lying on the loading ramp and it had since rained, effectively washing away any traces of blood.

On Friday, June 4th, Holbrook and Adwell drove to Vanderbilt Hospital in Nashville to continue their investigation. Upon their arrival they were introduced to Scotty's nurse, Ms. Kimberly Johnson, who directed them to his room for examination.

Scotty was lying on his back and in an induced coma. Only his forehead, eyes, nose, mouth and chin were visible due to the bandages on his head. Inserted in his body were a nasal gastric tube, a feeding tube, a catheter, an arterial line to draw blood, and a cerebral drip line.

Holbrook was given permission to examine his arms and legs for any other signs of injury. "Mr. Martin's nails were very short and almost cut to the quick," Holbrook later explained. "I noticed dried blood on the nails of his left hand. This blood appeared to be very old. I took a sample of the blood with a cotton swab and another control sample for comparison."

Because of the medical tubes and covers on his body, Holbrook was limited to examination but said he did not observe any injuries about Scotty's hands, upper arms, or lower extremities. He thanked the nurse, departed the room with Ranger Adwell, and was then introduced to Linda Sanders, Scotty's mother, outside. Holbrook explained that he was assisting the rangers with the investigation and would contact her should they need any further information. At this point they headed back home.

On Saturday, June 5th, Trooper Holbrook met Travis Adwell at the Austin Tracey Grocery Store in Austin, Kentucky, about fifteen miles south of Glasgow and only a few minutes drive from the State Park. Mr. Adwell was a first responder with the Austin Tracey Fire Department and one of the first people on the scene after John Moss's 911 call. He corroborated what the cook had said. "Martin was lying on his right side with his left arm resting on his head," Adwell explained. "His head was downhill toward the door of the loading dock and his back was facing the wall. There was a black bag under his arm with the strap around his neck. They couldn't find a buckle so it was cut from his body. Then they carried him up the ramp and placed him in an ambulance. His left arm and leg were the only parts of his body where movement was detected."

Nearly a week later on Thursday, June 10th, Sergeant Shannon West received a call from Ranger Adwell. He informed the sergeant that Scotty had died earlier that day and an autopsy would be conducted the following morning. Adwell surprised West by informing him that KSP would now be taking over the investigation. West explained he hadn't heard anything of the sort and would have to verify Adwell's claim with his superiors. Nevertheless, he would send one of his detectives to assist Adwell at the autopsy.

That evening, Captain Mayfield called Sergeant West at home and confirmed that KSP was indeed taking over the case. He requested that West lead the investigation and coordinate any resources and activities necessary to carry it out.

The following morning, West sent Detective Jaman Childers along with Adwell to the autopsy in Nashville. "I felt it was necessary for Ranger Adwell to attend the autopsy with Childers, given that we did not have an opportunity to process the scene," West said. "Adwell could answer specific questions that the medical examiner may have about the scene as it related to Martin's injury."

Getting back to work, Sergeant West contacted Scotty's father, Joel. Mr. Martin expressed his wishes for KSP to conduct a thorough investigation and explained that he was in possession of some of Scotty's personal effects that had been turned over to him by park rangers. He assured West that nothing had been touched and he would turn them over for further evaluation. They agreed to meet the following week.

Ninety miles away in Nashville, Detective Childers and Ranger Adwell arrived at the Medical Examiner's office to observe Scotty's autopsy. They met with Dr. Bruce Levy, who stated that he had reviewed the medical records and found that Scotty had suffered from a fracture of the occipital section of his skull. He said there was also bruising on both temporal lobes of the brain. In his experiences, he explained, "These types of injuries are consistent with a fall."

Adwell presented photos of the scene to Dr. Levy who took exceptional interest in the place where Scotty was discovered. He was also interested in the height of the wall from which it appeared Scotty had fallen.

Childers then accompanied Dr. Levy to the autopsy room where he took photographs of Scotty's body, beginning with his face, then his sides and back. Once all photos had been taken, the autopsy began.

During the initial examination, Dr. Levy discovered an untreated laceration on the back of Scotty's head. He shaved the area around the cut and photographs were taken of the injury. This injury was in the same location as the fracture that doctors had originally found. Dr. Levy examined the wound closely and pointed out the shape of it as being an "L." Together, Dr. Levy and Detective Childers compared the shape with the photograph of the concrete stop in the loading dock and speculated that it would have been consistent with Scotty's head striking the block. "It's strange. There was no mention of this injury in any of the proceeding medical records," Dr. Levy stated.

When the skull was made visible, the doctor pointed out to Childers that there was no fracture on the outside of the skull. Upon examination of the brain cavity, however, a fracture was discovered.

Detective Childers then spoke to Jonathan Knolton, the forensic technician who assisted during the autopsy. Mr. Knolton provided him with the clothing with which Scotty had been admitted. They were laid out so Childers could first take photographs. They included a black belt, black pants, blue dress shirt, black shoes and socks, and a white undershirt. He then packaged the clothes up and took them to Sergeant West back at Post 3.

As Childers was presenting the clothing to West, he noticed a scuffmark on the side of the right shoe that he hadn't noted before. The mark was on the instep and could have possibly been made by the concrete lip of the loading dock. Using a measuring device, he took photos of the scuffmark for future examination. West noted that Scotty's pants and shirt had apparently been cut off of him. "His pants were sliced up the side," Sergeant West said. "His zipper was unzipped approximately one quarter of its full length. Other than that, I noticed nothing significant, besides being blood-stained and somewhat soiled."

Childers also commented to Sergeant West that Dr. Levy noted there was no mention of the laceration in Martin's medical records, nor any evidence of treatment to the injury. According to Detective Childers, Dr. Levy found this to be remarkable. It was explained to West that the fracture to the inside of the skull, opposite the area where the blunt force trauma occurred, and no fracture to the outside surface of the skull under the laceration, was more conclusive evidence that the injury was consistent with a fall; all this courtesy of Dr. Levy.

After discussing the autopsy with Detective Childers, West asked Adwell for everything the rangers had with regard to their investigation, including notes, records, and photographs. Ranger Adwell referred to Trooper Holbrook, who had been assisting him, and stated that he had a lot of the information West was looking for. "In essence," Adwell said, "I didn't have a lot of details to offer."

According to Adwell's report, he was notified of the incident on Sunday, May 30, 2004 at around 7:15 a.m. The front desk clerk on duty had called to inform him of a man's body found behind the kitchen. Adwell arrived on the scene forty minutes later at 7:55 a.m. An ambulance and the Stat-Care helicopter were already on the Highland Games field. Emergency services personnel were working with the victim when he arrived. He identified the man as Jeremy Scott Martin.

He noted that Martin was at the Park to attend his Glasgow High School ten-year reunion. At that time, he contacted Ranger Hogue about the incident at approximately 9:15 a.m. His report reads as if the scene was taped off at that time, and he, Hogue, and Deputy Steve Runion of the Barren County Sheriff's Office took photographs.

Within his notepad, Adwell mentioned speaking with guests in cabins who attended the reunion. He noted Deputy Runion was told that someone had been picking on Martin earlier, but "would not give a name." Two guests, Angelo Pedicini and John Dickinson wrote out statements. Adwell summarized them as follows: "Mr. Martin was last seen between 0300 hours and 0400 hours at cabin #507. Blake Oliver and Bryant Vincent were in cabin #507 but left between 0600 hours and 0630 hours." Adwell was unable to locate Oliver or Vincent for questioning.

Adwell's notes go on to indicate that Martin went into the Lodge at approximately 3:30 a.m. and spoke to Stephen Foster, the desk clerk on duty. Martin asked Foster if he could use their phone to call a cab.

The final note on the page reports that the dining room supervisor at the Lodge had contacted Adwell in regards to one of the guests' request to speak to him. Mark Nelson, also attending the reunion, told the Ranger that there might have been some type of altercation between Martin, Blake Oliver, and Bryant Vincent.

On the following page Adwell indicated that he spoke with his supervisor, Captain Ed Furlong at 2:00 p.m. on Monday, May 31st. Furlong advised him to contact Kentucky State Police. This is when Adwell notes his phone call with Lieutenant Wolford and the decision of KSP not to get directly involved.

A summary of John Moss's statements was next and aligned with Trooper Holbrook's interview. But attached within Adwell's notes was an addendum to Moss's written statement. It read, "This man's glasses were about five feet away from his head, unbroken. I do not know if he fell from the above area or if he was walking down into the entrance way and tripped himself."

The next few pages of notes were written statements from four individuals. Mark Nelson wrote that he spoke to classmates who heard that Scotty had "sexually approached Blake Oliver and Bryant Vincent."

John Dickinson mentioned, simply, that Scotty left their cabin at 3:00 a.m. for approximately twenty minutes, returned, and then ultimately left again at 4:00 a.m.

Angelo Pedicini stated, too, that Scotty left Cabin 507 at 3:00 a.m. only to return shortly after; this before Angelo returned to Cabin 504 around 3:30 a.m.

Lastly, Stephen Foster stated that an unidentified female guest phoned him requesting allergy medication. This call was approximately 3:20 a.m. At 3:30 a.m., according to the clerk's records, a young man wearing a fanny pack walked to the front desk, asking for a phone. After using the phone, Foster said, "I asked him if he was with the group of locals going to the Indy 500 with Bobby Hurt. He told me he had called a cab."

West continued to review final records from Ranger Adwell, including a booklet from the reunion with photos and profiles of class members in attendance. There was no photo of Scotty, but his information was listed on the back cover. Also provided was a photocopy and list of its contents. There was $81 in cash in his wallet, according to this list. There were four twenty-dollar bills and a single one-dollar bill. There was also a bankcard, student ID, and a few various other cards. Included was a note that these items, including his cell phone, were turned over to Scotty's sister on May 30, 2004 at 4:46 p.m. It indicates Ranger Hogue as turning these over to Brandi, along with her initials.

...

On June 12th, Sergeant West visited the State Park to survey the scene for himself and to speak with prospective witnesses. He took digital photos of the loading dock and walked around the ledge of the retaining wall in the area where Scotty was found. He noted that the base of the loading dock had been thoroughly cleaned.

The loading dock is located at the rear of the Lodge. It is adjacent to the kitchen area. An eight-foot fence constructed along the cap of the concrete retaining wall separates the loading dock area from the rear door of Room #1 of the Lodge. The fence runs the length of the wall from the deepest portion of the dock towards the shallow entrance.

The dock goes from ground level approximately twelve feet down, under the rear portion of the Lodge. It is constructed of concrete with retaining walls on either side. It is utilized for trucks to load and unload supplies into the building. Near the bottom of this docking area are two concrete chock-blocks, which keep trucks from rolling back into the Lodge itself. The stops are approximately twelve inches in height and are affixed to the base of the loading dock.

West continued noting that the area is readily accessible to anyone who would venture into it. He mentions that there is no barrier fence on the right side (as is constructed on the left side) from which it appeared Scotty may have fallen. He states that there are no written warning signs posted or other barriers to limit access by guests or employees, which might alert them to this "potentially hazardous area."

"It is plausible," he said, "that the victim ventured back to this area where he could have easily fallen from the ledge to the base of the loading dock."

A few days later West would send Detective Kevin Pickett to investigate the same scene at night. In Pickett's report, he notes that he surveyed the area during the hours of darkness, "as this would have been the time that the incident involving Martin would have occurred."

Detective Pickett observes that the area where Scotty was discovered is not lit and would have been impossible to see him in the dark. He says although the first ten feet of the ramp is visible from the flood lamps at the kitchen door entrance, the concrete stops are not. Even after walking down the ramp he could not see them without the aid of a flashlight. Unfortunately, he writes that there are two lights beside the doors at the end of the ramp, but they were not illuminated. He also makes comments about the non-working security lights atop a radio tower near the door of the banquet room and a nearby light pole with a round, white globe; both inoperable and blackened on the inside.

. . .

On Sunday, June 13th, Sergeant West received a call from a fellow officer. He said, "At 7:55 p.m., Detective Forrest Winchester called me and told me that a Russellville Police Officer's friend, Ann Phelps, may have some information related to this investigation."

He soon called Mrs. Phelps to inquire and learned that she had attended Glasgow High School with Scotty Martin and the others. She told Sergeant West that she had been hearing rumors about Scotty from her brother, Clay Stovall, who was also from Glasgow but now living in Tennessee.

Ann told West that her brother had contacted David Downing, a close friend of his, in Glasgow, to find out what had happened during the reunion. He and Blake, according to Ann, were good friends.

Ultimately, Clay related to his sister what Blake had allegedly told David. She said Scotty was in a cabin with three guys: John Dickinson, Bryant Vincent, and Blake Oliver. Scotty, who Ann said is gay, offered Blake oral sex. He declined, but Bryant was alleged to have said something along the lines of, "If you want to suck on something, suck on this." This comment was directed toward Scotty as Bryant apparently pointed to his crotch. Scotty then performed oral sex on Bryant.

Ann goes on to say that Bryant's wife, who was supposedly asleep in the next room, was awakened and found out what had just happened with her husband and Scotty. There was an argument between the couple, and Scotty quickly left the cabin. She finished her statements by telling Sergeant West that her information was purely rumor, with no firsthand knowledge on her part. West decided to go directly to David Downing for a statement.

"I don't want to talk to you," Downing told West after opening his front door. "I'm Blake's friend, and I don't wanna speak about the matter."

"I can leave at any point," West explained, "but Detective Pickett told me what a good guy you were, and that we could count on you to help us in this case."

David stepped outside.

West continued, "I know Blake has talked to you. I'm merely trying to find out the facts concerning what really occurred."

Downing admitted he had spoken to Blake regarding what had happened with Scotty. He was adamant that he knew Blake was telling him the truth; that Blake had nothing to do with Scotty's injuries.

"Blake's a good person," Downing said. "I believe that."

Despite Sergeant West's efforts, Downing refused to explain what Blake had told him.

"Blake's attorney's not doing any good in discouraging him from cooperating with the police," West said. "If he didn't have anything to do with Scotty's injuries, he shouldn't be concerned in helping us get to the bottom of what happened.

Downing said he would try to get Blake to do the right thing.

"If he doesn't talk to you," Downing told West, "then I'm willing to share what he told me about that night."

And with that statement, West headed back to the office.

. . .

On Tuesday, June 15th, Sergeant West asked Detective Pickett to contact Blake Oliver, John Dickinson, and Bryant Vincent. He noted that all three men have family in Glasgow. Later that afternoon, West met with Karen Davis in reference to the investigation. While discussing some of the details of the case, Davis mentioned that she has subpoenaed all phone records, as well as medical records. She had also obtained the 911 tape of John Moss's call. Davis concluded the meeting by saying that she had heard John Dickinson and Blake Oliver wanted to speak to law enforcement about the incident.

At 2:30 p.m. Detective Pickett arrived at the Glasgow City Building and spoke to Blake's mother, Shelia Oliver, the City Clerk. He told Mrs. Oliver that he was assisting in the investigation at the State Park that involved the subsequent death of Scotty Martin. Blake's mother told the detective how very upset her family was over the incident. She also mentioned the many rumors circulating about her son, as well as John and Bryant.

"On Sunday morning," Mrs. Oliver said, "I was sitting in my kitchen, reading the paper and drinking coffee. I heard someone knock on the kitchen window and saw that it was Blake." She said she recalled the time to be about 9:00 a.m. or 9:30 a.m.

"I asked him why he was there," she continued. "He replied that all the beds were full in the cabin, and he just wanted to sleep because he had been up all night. He said that everyone had been talking and having a good time."

She then called Blake at work and handed the phone to Detective Pickett. Blake told the officer that he was more than willing to talk, and all the rumors about him connected to the death were untrue. Pickett gave Blake Sergeant West's number to arrange an interview. The conversation ended with Blake stating that he wanted to get it over with.

On Pickett's departure, Mrs. Oliver mentioned, "Blake has really been upset over all this. He wanted to go to the funeral but didn't because he felt like Scotty's family thought he had something to do with it."

At 3:15 p.m. Sergeant West was back at the State Park interviewing the business manager, Judy Lowe. He had heard unsubstantiated rumors that all the occupants of Cabin 507 were gone as of 7:00 a.m. He asked Mrs. Lowe if she could obtain check-out records for those in that particular cabin. She pulled a receipt for Blake Oliver. The departure date and time was May 30, 2004 at 2:49 p.m.

"In many instances," Mrs. Lowe explained to Sergeant West, "guests don't actually come to the desk and check out. 2:49 p.m. was most likely the time housekeeping personnel got to the room for cleaning."

On June 16th, West called Blake and left a message, asking him to call back regarding an interview. Blake returned the call immediately with a request for Sergeant West. He wanted to meet in person at the mayor's office in Glasgow at 1:00 p.m. Realizing a prior commitment, West suggested the meeting take place instead at his post in Bowling Green, but Blake declined.

"You don't have to speak with me at all," West told Blake, "but I know you've been wanting to get things cleared up about the death of Scotty Martin."

Blake admitted that a "prominent judge" had called and given him three pieces of advice. "He told me not to talk to police, don't take a polygraph, and don't go to the police station or participate in the investigation."

West returned, "If you didn't have anything to do with Martin's death, then you shouldn't have anything to fear in clearing some things up for us."

"It's just that I was one of the last persons to see Scotty," Blake admitted.

Ultimately, the two agreed to meet the following morning at the mayor's office, but Blake ended up canceling.

"He left me a voicemail stating that his employer required him to work Thursday and Friday," West explained. "He said he would contact me the following week, but he failed to do that as well."

Hours later, West attempted to work out a time and place to interview John Dickinson. He told West that he had been advised to seek counsel prior to any questioning.

At 10:00 p.m. the Sergeant contacted Taylor Bale Kuczynski by phone. Taylor had been the class president, was currently living in Boulder, Colorado, and was the organizer of the reunion. She explained to Sergeant West many of the same, minor details that others had mentioned.

"Everything started around 6:00 p.m.," she began. "The reunion itself was in Room #1 of the Lodge. Everyone was having a really good time, and things were going well. I wasn't aware of any conflicts or arguments throughout the evening. My husband, David, and I went to bed around midnight in Cabin 510."

She went on to say that Blake had rented Cabin 507, which is where everyone had gone after the reunion activities ended. She had heard that Bryant Vincent, John Dickinson, Blake Oliver, Chris York, and Scotty Martin were in this cabin. She went on to describe some of the rumors she had heard from other, unnamed classmates.

"Around 4:00 a.m. or 4:30 a.m., Bryant made a pass at Scotty," she said. "They ended up in another room of the cabin where they were alone. I guess John or Blake opened the door and found Bryant with his pants down. There was some kind of confrontation, and Scotty left."

Taylor noted that what she heard were just rumors, but it did make her wonder if any foul play had actually occurred.

"The phone rang at 7:00 a.m., and someone on the other end told me that there had been an accident and I needed to come to the loading dock as soon as possible." She said she and David got dressed, headed to the Lodge, and immediately noticed Scotty lying at the bottom of the ramp in a pool of blood.

West told her that witnesses had heard her remark that it was all her fault.

"I just felt responsible because I had organized the event, and if I had done something differently this might not have happened," she said. "But I know that's not realistic."

. . .

The next morning, Sergeant West met Steve Runyon, the Barren County Deputy Sheriff, who reported to the State Park on the morning of May 30th.

"I was notified around 8:00 a.m. when I came on duty," Runyon began. "I called Larry Bragg back from the Austin Tracy Volunteer Fire Department but ended up talking to Ranger Adwell instead."

Runyon told West that Adwell insisted he come to the Park and take the investigation. "I told the Ranger that he was trained just like we were, and that they needed to start doing some of their own investigations. But I agreed to assist them."

When Runyon arrived, he instructed Ranger Adwell to clear the immediate scene. "There were several guests, EMS workers, etc. who didn't need to be there at that point. I ended up helping Adwell and Ranger Hogue take some photos."

At that point West pulled out the photographs that Ranger Adwell had turned over, and the two men began to look through them together. Runyon acknowledged that he had taken the majority of them and initialed the backs of the ones he remembered shooting.

One photo in particular seemed to catch the eye of Sergeant West. In it, an ink pen is shown pointing to some type of small object West believed to have been flesh or brain matter. Deputy Runyon identified it as chewing gum.

"I urged Ranger Hogue to collect that as evidence," Runyon stated. "He made a comment about collecting a sample of the congealed blood on the chock-block, but I told him not to concern himself about that 'cause we knew who's blood it was. I reminded him again to get that gum."

West knew that his office had not yet obtained this piece of evidence. He instructed Runyon to write a detailed report with regard to his actions and include everything he and West had discussed.

Before interviewing the EMS crew that prepared Scotty for the Stat-Flight to Nashville, West reviewed the related Medical Service Report. The chief complaint on the report was listed as "Fall Severe Head Trauma and/or Head Injury." Scotty's physical condition was noted as "breathing-decreased, skin-pale and cool to the touch, pupils-constricted and non-reactive, pulse-left carotid (present)."

The summary of his condition on the following page indicated that he fell "approximately 12-15 feet onto the concrete, possibly up to 4 hours prior to EMS arrival." Scotty's pupils are noted as being constricted and fixed while his lungs were clear. He had a large amount of blood at the back of his head, but none coming from his nose or ears. Oral intubation was attempted but, his teeth were clinched.

Jason Blakely, who wrote the report, later spoke to Sergeant West. "When I arrived, the Fire Department was still immobilizing him. When they cut off his clothes I remembered seeing an abrasion on his left or right arm, along the forearm, near the elbow. Then, when the flight medic arrived, I discovered a one- to two-inch tear in the back of this throat."

Blakely explained that this could have resulted from the injury to the back of Scotty's head.

West asked, "How long do you think Scotty had been lying there?"

"Probably an hour or more based upon the blood congealing. The blood on the concrete had already started drying and was black around the edges."

That afternoon Sergeant West and Detective Pickett met with Scotty's father to obtain evidence given back to him by Ranger Adwell. Mr. Martin handed over a white, cardboard box with broken, red evidence tape around it. Inside the box was a plastic biohazard bag containing Scotty's bloody fanny pack, along with its contents. Detective Pickett later inventoried those items: a blue velvet-covered silver dollar box containing a suspected controlled substance, a Glasgow High School reunion booklet, three compact discs, a packet of Orbit peppermint chewing gum with 12 of 14 pieces, lip balm, hairspray and a black ink pen. Sergeant West took possession of the items and later stored them at his post.

Before he left, Scotty's father stated that he thought it was odd that the evidence had been returned to him so soon after Scotty's death and was adamant that he didn't touch or go through it. He went on to say that he had heard nothing new but suggested the detectives contact Scotty's cousin, who also attended the reunion.

Later that day, Sergeant West interviewed Michelle Huffman, Scotty's third cousin. She told the officer that Scotty arrived at the Lodge around 7:30 p.m. He had gotten a ride from Amy Claywell Sawyer, whose brother married Scotty's sister. Michelle told West that Scotty had called her prior to the reunion.

"He was apprehensive about it," she said. "He wanted to ensure I was going to be there."

Michelle agreed that he was in good spirits and everyone seemed to be having a good time. She left around 10:30 p.m., not before telling him goodbye. She went on to say that she was made aware of the incident from Stacey Renfro Phillips, who called Sunday morning and informed her that Scotty had been hurt. Michelle also stated that, over the course of the next few hours, she began hearing rumors that something happened involving Bryant Vincent. While she left messages for him at home in Alabama, her calls were not returned. She also handed over a photo to Sergeant West. It was one that she had taken that evening and showed a group of guys posing at the reunion. West found it noteworthy that all persons of interest and key witnesses were present in the picture.

West later made contact with the Yellow Cab dispatcher, John Key, who was working the night Scotty allegedly called for a taxi. He verified that he cancelled the call after not being able to confirm it on call back at approximately 4:14 a.m. "I tried calling the number," Key said, "but it came back as some kind of pre-paid cellular company. I called and asked my driver if he still wanted to go, but he declined since we weren't able to verify if the person still needed a cab."

. . .

West arrived at the office of attorney Bobby Richardson on Wednesday, June 23rd, after receiving word that he was representing John Dickinson. Richardson stated to West that former Barren County judge, Benny Dickinson, had advised John not to speak to police without an attorney. Benny, as it turned out, was also John's uncle. The three men agreed to meet at Richardson's office on July 2nd.

At the beginning of John Dickinson's interview, Richardson asked West if his client was the target of a criminal investigation.

"I explained that I was conducting a non-criminal death investigation," West said.

"Do you have an autopsy report?" Richardson asked.

West replied, "I do not. The medical examiner's office hasn't determined the manner of death, pending my investigation."

And with that, Mr. Richardson established that he would be in control of the interview.

West started his questioning by asking John to give him a detailed account of what had happened the night of May 29th through the morning of May 30th. John explained that he and his wife, Ellody, had gone to his reunion and invited several people back to their cabin afterwards.

"It ended up that a lot more people showed up. Then around 3:00 a.m. it started to thin out a little bit."

John said that the people staying at the cabin at that time were he and his wife, who was already in bed, Stacey and Andrew McChord who were both in bed, Bryant Vincent, his wife Holli, who was asleep, and Chris York who was also in bed.

"The ones still awake were me, Blake Oliver, Bryant, Angelo Pedicini, and Scotty. We were all sitting on the front porch screwing around with a skunk," he said.

He told Sergeant West that Blake went inside the cabin, and he assumed he was going to sleep. "Then I saw Scotty follow Blake inside, only to come back out a few seconds later. He walked right by us and up the hill."

West asked John to describe what happened next.

"Right after Scotty left, Blake came outside and told us that Scotty had made a pass at him."

"What time was this?" West asked.

"Around 3:30 a.m.," John replied.

West asked, "Can you be more specific about the pass?"

John explained that Scotty had offered Blake oral sex. He went on to say that Blake was not upset about it. "We just sorta joked and laughed about it," John said.

"Then what occurred?" West inquired.

"Angelo left and went back to his cabin, and Bryant and Blake and I went back inside. A few minutes later, Scotty came back in, too. He headed toward the kitchen area and just sat there for a while. This was about 4:00 a.m. I guess. Then Scotty came over to Bryant who was laying on the couch and tried to give him a blowjob."

West asked, "What did you do?"

"I stood up and said 'I'm outta here'," John replied. He recounts that he left the cabin and headed to the top of the hill about fifty feet from the porch. "About fifteen seconds later I see Scotty come out and head in the direction of the Lodge."

John tells West that he walked back into the cabin where he, Bryant, and Blake laughed about it. He said Bryant's wife woke up at that point and "made" him come to bed. Ellody got up around the same time Holli did and asked John to come to bed too, he explained. Instead, he and Blake stayed up and talked about what had happened.

"We cleaned up the cabin, picked up all the garbage and took it up the hill about sixty feet away where the trash cans are located. Then we just sat on the porch and watched the sun come up. Eventually I helped Blake put a refrigerator in the back of his car. We were trading a large one for a smaller one. Then we went back to the cabin, and I told Blake I was going to bed."

"What did he say?" West asked.

"He said he wasn't sleeping on the couch; that he was going to his parents' house instead."

West inquired, "What time was it as this point"

"Around 7:00 a.m.," John replied.

"Was anyone excessively intoxicated that night?" West asked.

"Not excessively, no," he said.

West asked John about Blake's disposition after being propositioned by Scotty.

"He was more taken aback," he said.

"And Bryant's?" West inquired.

"He was irritated," John said, "but not mad."

Sergeant West then asked John if Bryant was still there around 7:00 a.m. John said Chris York apparently spoke to the Vincents that morning, prior to going to the Lodge for breakfast, thus he supposed Bryant was still there, at least until around 7:00 a.m.

When asked if he remembered who told him about Scotty that morning, John said that a park ranger had come to his cabin around 10:00 a.m.

"Prior to that," he said, "Mark Nelson told me that Scotty had been in an accident. This was around 7:00 a.m."

"What did Mr. Nelson say?" he asked.

John replied, "He asked me if there was any kind of an assault involving anyone there and Scotty. I told him no."

West explained to John that he needed to know how far the apparent act of oral sex described went. West believed that it was important to establish a motive, or lack thereof, if Bryant invited it.

John told West that he could not honestly answer the question as his back was to Scotty when he knelt down next to Bryant. He simply said he got up and walked out. John denied, however, that Bryant made any comments inviting Scotty to give him oral sex.

"Did anyone leave the cabin after Scotty left the second time," West asked.

"No one," John said, "Just me and Blake, to take the garbage."

West asked John if he had any contact with Bryant since the incident. John explained that he had spoken to him on two or three occasions in reference to everything going around. He commented to Sergeant West that he insisted to Bryant that they needed to tell the whole truth about what had occurred.

West asked a final question. "Why would Taylor Bale Kuczynski say that everyone was gone from the cabin when she came by around 7:30 a.m.?"

"That's completely wrong," John stated. "The only explanation for that could be that she knocked on the door, and on one answered. She didn't come inside. Or maybe some of them had gone to breakfast by the time she got there."

West stated that, during the interview, John appeared cooperative, and although there were discrepancies with his time frames, West noted "the discrepancies appear to be more akin to not keeping up with what time it was as the night and early morning hours progressed."

The following day, West heard again from Blake. He told the Sergeant that he was willing to cooperate and had retained Glasgow attorney Tim Gillenwater. "My mom insisted I retain counsel prior to giving any kind of statement to the police," Blake told West. "My attorney told me not to contact you any further but wanted you to know that we are still interested in cooperating with the investigation by giving you an interview."

However, On June 29th, Blake's attorney called West saying he was reluctant to allow his client to speak to him. "In essence,' West stated, "Mr. Gillenwater didn't see anything his client had to gain in being interviewed. I contented that Mr. Oliver should be interviewed, but it was obviously his choice in the matter."

...

On June 24th, Sergeant West received the subpoenaed medical records from Vanderbilt Hospital. Those records confirmed much of what Dr. Levy had originally stated. Scotty suffered no internal injuries, contusions, broken bones or fractures. There was, as previously reported, an abrasion on Scotty's right arm near the elbow and a small abrasion in the suprapubic area.

West could not find a toxicology or blood screen report within the documents. "I believe a blood toxicology report would give some idea of what level, if any, of alcohol was in Martin's system," he explained, "or any other controlled substances." He contacted the hospital, which in turn, said they would look into the matter and try to locate these documents, if they existed.

On Friday, Sergeant West interviewed his first witness in the investigation, Mark Nelson. He explained to West that he had attended the reunion with Megan Bale, Taylor Bale Kucynski's younger sister. He described everyone getting along well and was not aware of any problems between guests.

"A lot of people ended up at Cabin 507 after the reunion was over," Mark began. "I went to bed around 3:00 p.m. in Cabin 504. Around 7:00 a.m. David Kucynski was knocking on our door and told us that Scotty had been hurt in an accident. He told me that Scotty had fallen off a loading dock and was really messed up. I think he said they were trying to get in touch with his parents."

Mark went on to say that everyone got dressed and walked to the loading dock around 8:00 a.m. He said they arrived on the scene as the ambulance was leaving, then headed towards the Lodge for breakfast.

"After eating, some of us walked back to the dock and noticed the rangers taping off the scene," he said.

"Do you remember what time that was?" West asked.

"It had to have been around 9:00 a.m. 'cause we were in the Lodge for a while," he answered. "I remember talking to Rangers Adwell and Hogue. They asked what cabin we were in and took down my information. Then, as we headed back there, I saw Chris York in the parking lot. He was tying down his motorcycle in his truck."

Sergeant West asked, "Did you talk to him?"

"Yes," Mark replied, "I told him that the rangers would probably be coming down there and he needed to get their beer cans cleaned up. He asked me why the rangers were coming down, and I told him because of Scotty."

"What did Chris say then?" West inquired.

"He said, 'To hell with Scotty'; that he had come on to Bryant and Blake the night before. I hadn't heard any of this until Chris told me."

West asked, "And what was Chris's reaction?"

"He was apparently unaware of what had happened to Scotty until I told him," Mark replied.

Mark went on to say that after talking to Chris they proceeded to Cabin 507 and woke up John Dickinson and his wife as well as Stacey and Andrew McChord, who were also staying in the cabin.

"John said something to the effect that he was a changed man after seeing that last night," Mark said. "I assumed he meant he saw Scotty make a pass to Blake and Bryant."

West then asked, "Did you see either of those boys that morning?"

Mark replied, "No."

After speaking to the Dickinsons and the McChords, Mark said he went back to his cabin and noted that he stayed an additional night. He told West that he had spoken again to the rangers.

"I contacted Ranger Adwell later that night and told him I felt compelled to let them know that there had been some rumors circulating. I never thought Scotty's incident was more than an accident until I started to hear what everyone else had been saying."

In his notes, Sergeant West indicated that Mark seemed genuinely interested in providing information with regards to circumstances surrounding Scotty's injuries. "He was able to corroborate that the Dickinsons, McChords, and Chris York were still at Cabin 507 during the late morning hours of May 30th," West wrote. "He also confirmed that he did not see Bryant or Blake that morning, and that York apparently did not know about Scotty's injury until he told him."

Prior to Mark's interview, Sergeant West had attempted to speak with Chris himself. He showed up at Chris's apartment around 7:00 p.m. and asked him if he knew why he was there.

"He said he did," West noted. "He told me that he wanted to help, but that his parents had insisted he have his attorney, Walter Baker, present when he did. I told him he didn't have to give me any kind of statement; that I was just trying to get to the bottom of all the rumors about him."

At this point, Chris invited Sergeant West inside. "He told me that everyone was getting along fine and that he went to bed earlier than the others staying in the cabin. When I asked him more specific questions he said he wasn't comfortable without his attorney. I told him I'd call Mr. Baker and set up a time to meet. He was fine by that and I left."

The following Tuesday, West phoned Ranger Hogue. "I asked him if he recalled collecting the chewing gum that Deputy Runyon photographed as evidence. He said he didn't," West reported. "I told him that Runyon said to be sure to collect the gum on two separate occasions during the time they were processing the scene on May 30th. Hogue said he didn't remember the deputy telling him that and he didn't collect any gum. He said they must have had 'miscommunication'."

Later, West contacted Sherry Saint at the Tennessee Medical Examiner's Office in reference to toxicology reports. She advised him that she wasn't sure if any tests were performed on Scotty due to his prolonged stay in the hospital.

"If admissions blood is pulled by the emergency room," she explained, "it is generally discarded after seven days. Mr. Martin died ten days after he was admitted."

West asked Ms. Saint if she would have Dr. Levy call him back regarding that report and to answer a few other questions he had. She agreed to do so.

Chris York met Sergeant West at the office of attorney Walter Baker on July 2nd. West stated later that Chris seemed cordial and genuine in wanting to give an account of what he knew about the circumstances surrounding Scotty's injuries.

"The reunion ended around midnight," Chris began. "Several people came back to our cabin and were drinking. Everybody was getting along. Then I went to bed around 2:00 a.m."

"What time did you wake up?" West asked.

"I woke up around 9:00 a.m. or 10:00 a.m.," Chris said. "As soon as I walked out of the bedroom, the first thing anyone said to me was 'Oh, you'll never believe what happened last night.'"

West inquired, "Who was there when you woke up?"

Chris thought for a second, then said, "John and Ellody Dickinson, Bryant and Holli Vincent, and Stacey and Andrew McChord."

"What did they tell you?" West asked.

"John told me that Scotty had come on to Blake and Bryant," he explained. "He told me that Scotty offered Blake a blowjob and that he made sexual advances toward Bryant."

"What did you think about that?" West asked Chris.

"We were joking and laughing about it. We couldn't believe that had happened," Chris said.

West asked, "Then what did you do?"

"I went out to the parking lot and started tying my motorcycle down to my truck 'cause I was leaving for South Carolina to meet my family on vacation. Then I saw Mark Nelson coming towards me, and he asked me if I had heard about Scotty."

"What did you tell him?" West asked.

"I told him I had heard that he was hitting on everyone in the cabin and started laughing," Chris said. "But then Mark told me that Scotty had been found in a pool of blood, and that they didn't think he was going to make it. I felt like an ass after laughing about it."

West asked Chris to elaborate further on who was still at the cabin when he got up that morning.

Chris responded, "John Dickinson and his wife Ellody, Bryant and Holli Vincent, and Stacey and Andrew McChord. The Vincents were getting up around the same time I did. Blake wasn't there when I woke up."

West questioned Chris again about any sort of altercation that he might have been told of by anyone concerning Scotty. He told the sergeant that he was not aware of anything of that nature.

"What was Bryant's attitude about the sexual advances," West asked.

Chris replied, "He was chuckling about the whole thing, but he wasn't angry about it."

"How far did the advances go?" West asked.

"Scotty got down in Bryant's lap," Chris started, "but John told me he didn't know if Scotty got Bryant's penis in his mouth or not. John said he got up at that point and went outside. Then John said about thirty seconds later Scotty came outside and walked away. That was the last time they saw him."

Later in the week, Sergeant West phoned the McChords for a joint interview. Stacey answered and began relaying some of the rumors that she had heard regarding what allegedly occurred at the cabin. Much of the rumors revolved around Scotty's alleged sexual advances directed at Blake and Bryant.

"My husband and I went to bed around 2:30 a.m.," Stacey explained, "At around 3:00 a.m., Blake opened the door to our bedroom, laughing, and telling us that Scotty had just offered him a blowjob. Then he shut the door and we went back to sleep."

Stacey went on to say that she did not recall much after that as anything she knew first hand. She was aware that Scotty was at the cabin and everyone was getting along.

"I recall that Mark Nelson and Chris York came to the cabin the next morning around 8:30 a.m. or 9:00 a.m.," she said. "The Dickinsons had slept in, and I remember that Blake and the Vincents were gone by that time."

Feeling like he had heard enough from Stacey, West asked to speak with her husband.

Andrew McChord was not a graduate of that class and had only made acquaintances with those involved in the investigation. He told Sergeant West much of the same things Stacey had said.

"However," Andrew told West, "I do recall lying in bed and not being able to sleep. I think this was around 3:00 a.m. I overheard Bryant talking to some of the others. I suspected it was Blake and John."

"What did you hear?" West asked.

Andrew answered, "I recall hearing Bryant say something to the effect of 'Hey, he just pulled it out of my shorts and put it in his mouth.'"

"Could you describe the tone in which this statement was made," West inquired.

Andrew replied, "A defensive tone."

. . .

On July 1st, Sergeant West spoke to Dr. Bruce Levy, who answered several of the detective's questions with regards to Scotty's injuries.

West began, "Could the head injury Scotty sustained have resulted from being pushed down, at ground level, where he fell backwards, striking his head on the concrete chock-blocks?"

"No, it is not likely Scotty was pushed down at ground level with regard to the type and severity of his injury," Dr. Levy replied.

West continued, "Could Scotty have been head slammed by someone who had him by the hair and forced his head onto the chock-block?"

"He could have been head slammed," Dr. Levy explained, "with his head against the corner of the chock-block, yet his injury is more consistent with his head moving and striking a stationary object and not a moving object striking his head."

The doctor continued his explanation. "In all other cases I've seen, where someone's head was slammed or forced into some stationary object, there was always more than one injury associated with multiple blows. Furthermore, it would be remarkable and unusual that no other injuries precipitated such action, for example, injuries sustained during a struggle to get someone to the position in which to force their head into a stationary object."

West asked, "Is it more or less probable that Scotty fell from a variable height?"

"It is more probable," Dr. Levy said, "that Scotty fell from a height; however, a specific height cannot be determined. Nonetheless, it is obvious that the greater the height, the more probable serious injury or injuries are to occur."

"Finally," West asked the doctor, "if he likely fell from the top of the retaining wall, approximately eleven feet, why didn't he sustain any other substantial injuries?"

Dr. Levy simply expressed, "It is not extraordinary, remarkable, or significant that Scotty did not present more injuries."

Given his experience, Dr. Levy explained that it is within the norm to find a single injury where all or most of the force is absorbed in that one area. He noted a recent case in Nashville where a man fell from a second story balcony and landed on his face. He had no other noteworthy injuries other than a broken skull directly related to where his body first impacted the ground.

With regard to toxicology, Dr. Levy told the Sergeant they did not draw blood in this case, due to Scotty having been in the hospital for such a significant amount of time prior to his eventual death.

"Furthermore," Dr. Levy said, "we did not receive any admissions blood from Vanderbilt Hospital either. They discard it after seven days."

Sergeant West finally determined that it appeared no toxicology was ever performed on Scotty. The doctor told West that his final report was pending "Matter of Death" in reference to the conclusions of KSP's investigation. West told Dr. Levy he would finalize that report once he had completed the case.

. . .

On July 7th, Sergeant West and Detective Mike Yates visited the home of Bryant and Holli Vincent in Hoover, Alabama for a scheduled interview. After introductions were made, Sergeant West asked the Vincents if they would mind interviewing them separately. They agreed, and Bryant went first.

"My wife and son and I arrived in Glasgow a couple of days prior to the reunion and stayed at my parents' house. Then on the 29th we showed up at our cabin around 5:30 p.m. From there we headed over to the reunion at the Lodge. There were about eighty to a hundred people there, I guess. Anyway, we ate dinner and hung out with some of my friends. Then about midnight the reunion was over, and people started heading over to our cabin. About twenty to twenty-five people showed up."

West made notes as Bryant described the events of the evening. He finally told the sergeant he would cut to the chase.

"Around 1:30 a.m. or 2:00 a.m., Blake came out of the cabin and said to John Dickinson, 'Hey, Scotty Martin just made a pass at me,'" Bryant explained. "Blake was just laughing about it."

"What did John say?" West asked.

"Dickinson's response was, 'Yeah, right,'" he said. "But Blake kept saying, 'I'm serious, I'm serious.'"

Bryant described their response as, "Yeah, whatever," because Scotty was only three to four people in proximity to himself, Blake and John while Blake was describing the incident.

"We were out in front of the cabin," Bryant explained, "during that time. So were Angelo Pedicini, Mark Nelson, Matt Garrett, and Anne Gentry. There were probably around fifteen people outside when Blake said that about Scotty. And Scotty wasn't saying anything. He was just acting like nothing ever happened. To me, that would be a little awkward."

Bryant went on to say that, for the next hour or so, everyone just hung out on the porch with no problems.

"I remembered this to a tee," Bryant started up again, "Scotty was just sitting there with his arms crossed, up against the deck. I told him to get a beer. He did and everything was cool, no problems."

Around 2:00 a.m. or so everybody started leaving the cabin, he explained, and his wife told him that she was going to bed. Bryant commented to West that he really was not paying attention to the time. He, Angelo, Scotty, Blake, and John were the only ones left on the porch. Angelo told them he was calling it a night and going back to his cabin.

"The others agreed to go inside," Bryant said, referring to cabin 507.

"Describe the scene inside," West asked.

Bryant stated, "John was sitting in a corner of the living room area in a chair of some sort. Blake was on the love seat, covered up, because that's where he was sleeping. I was on the couch in my boxer shorts, and we were all just watching television."

"Where was Scotty?" West asked.

"He was in the kitchen at the table. The light was off in there, and I didn't even know he was in there at first," Bryant explained. "He comes out of nowhere, gets on his knees beside the couch I'm on, reaches for my penis and asks, 'Can I give you a blowjob?'"

"And how did you respond?" West asked.

"I said, 'Hey, I'm not into that.' I told him my wife was in the next room, and if I wanted a blowjob I could go in there," Bryant said.

Bryant then described Scotty as getting up and leaving the cabin at that time.

"I asked John, 'Can you believe that just happened?' he said. "Blake and John and I were just laughing about the whole thing."

Bryant goes on to say that he walked to his wife's bedroom where she was asleep, woke her up, and told her what Scotty had just done. He told West that Holli did not believe him at first. He described her actions as having come into the living room area, sitting down, and talking to them about what had happened.

"That right there is the end of the story," Bryant said. "We went to bed after that."

Bryant stated they woke up the following morning and got ready to leave. He noted that Blake was gone. He told West they were driving back to Alabama that day and had to pick his son up at his mother's house. He said he assumed John was still asleep. They got ready, loaded their vehicle, and left.

"On the way back to Alabama," Bryant said, "John called and told us that police were questioning everyone with regard to an accident in which Scotty was seriously injured."

Detective Yates digressed by asking Bryant more specific questions with regard to the instance when Scotty attempted to perform oral sex on him. He asked if there was any related violence. Bryant insisted there was no violence, no punches thrown, no harsh words, nothing. "He just got up and left,' Bryant said.

Detective Yates asked, "Did Scotty say anything to John or Blake?"

"No," Bryant said. "He just left the cabin." He stated this occurred around 3:00 a.m., and he did not know where Scotty was going when he took off.

"Who witnessed this incident?" Yates asked.

Bryant replied, "John and Blake."

Bryant went on to say that he and Holli had left the cabin around 9:00 a.m. and arrived at his mother's house around 10:00 a.m. to pick up his son. Bryant's mother, Mary, would later confirm to police that she did, in fact, arrive home from church service around 10:00 a.m. to 10:30 a.m. that morning. She explained that her son and Holli were both at her residence when she returned home, then left shortly thereafter because Bryant had to be back at work Monday morning.

"Did you have any plans to stick around Glasgow later than Sunday?" Yates asked.

"No, because my football team had workouts on Monday the 31st. I had to be in at 8:00 a.m."

Detective Yates asked, "Have you talked to John Dickinson since he first told you about Scotty's injuries?"

"I have," Bryant replied.

"What does he have to say about it?" Yates asked.

Bryant said, "He just wants it to be over. He said we don't have anything to worry about."

Bryant explained to the detectives that John's uncle said to be sure to have an attorney present if they talked to police. John apparently told Bryant to have an attorney "just in case." He went on to say that he had some friends in Alabama who told him that if he did not have anything to hide then he did not need an attorney.

Yates asked, "Did you speak to anyone prior to leaving the cabin?"

"Chris was still there when we left. We woke him up to tell him we were leaving," Bryant said.

Yates jumped around the questioning again, "Did Scotty make physical contact with you?"

Bryant tried to explain, "He reached and grabbed my penis out of my shorts, but he didn't get it in his mouth."

At this point West asked Bryant, "When this occurred, did you look at Blake or John and ask something to the order of 'Do you want any of this action?'"

"I didn't say that," Bryant said. "I did add, however, 'I ain't into this. Blake, John, are you into this?' Maybe that's what someone heard."

Yates asked, "What did you hear happened to Scotty?"

Bryant answered, "I heard he climbed a fence or something and fell into a loading dock. I heard he didn't have any scratches or bruises or any signs of a fight, just where he landed on his head. I heard that Scotty had called a taxi to pick him up, but when it arrived, no one saw him, so the taxi left. They flew Scotty to Vanderbilt, he had brain damage or swelling to the brain, and he was in a coma. They didn't know if he was going to make it or not, and if he did, he would be a vegetable. Then I heard he died, that he didn't make it."

West asked Bryant, "Did you hear anything about drug use?"

"I did hear that he was doing ecstasy and cocaine; that they found both in his system," he responded.

West asked him if he heard that from a reliable source or someone else. Bryant explained that Bobby Lee Hurt, the Barren River Lake Park

Manager, had told Blake's mother that Scotty had these drugs in his system.

Yates asked Bryant, "What were you guys talking about when the sexual advance occurred?"

"I don't know," Bryant said.

West interjected, "It doesn't make sense to me that Scotty would do what he did without some conversation that would give him the idea that his advances would be accepted. Do you recall any conversation Scotty had with John or Blake of a sexual nature?"

Bryant thought for a moment. As if by revelation, he said he recalled a commercial for "Girls Gone Wild" videos on TV when Scotty came out from the kitchen.

"Scotty said something to the effect of 'Boys Gone Wild'," Bryant said. "That's when he reached for my penis."

"How long did that particular incident last," West asked.

"No time," Bryant said.

"And what about John or Blake's position?" Yates asked, "Could either one of them tell if your penis was in Scotty's mouth?"

"I don't think so," Bryant said, again describing their locations in the room.

Yates stated, "I have a witness who told us that he overheard you make the comment to Blake and John, in a defensive tone, 'Man, all I know is he got my penis out of my shorts and into his mouth before I knew it.'"

Bryant shook his head. "No," he said, "that didn't happen. He got my penis out, he grabbed for it, he got it, but no, not in his mouth."

The two detectives then shifted the questioning to how Holli was made aware of the incident.

Yates asked pointedly, "Did Holli wake on her own or did you awaken her?"

"I woke her up," Bryant said, "and told her about what had just happened."

"Was there any exchange of words after Scotty's advance?" West asked.

Bryant told them, "No, he just got up and left."

Sergeant West then talked to Bryant about taking a polygraph exam. Bryant indicated that he would voluntarily take one, and they ultimately agreed upon a date. Then the questioning resumed.

"Would anyone at the reunion tell us that you, Blake, or John were picking on Scotty that night?" Yates asked.

Bryant shook his head again, "No."

"Did you know Scotty was openly gay?" West asked.

"No, I didn't know that," Bryant answered.

"Not trying to be facetious," West began, "but what was your first clue that Scotty was a homosexual?"

Bryant answered, "When Blake told us that Scotty had propositioned him. He was in the band in school, always in a girl crowd. We always wondered but didn't give it much more thought than that."

Yates asked, "So what do you think happened to Scotty?"

Bryant began speaking of the incident in the cabin when Scotty made sexual advances toward him. "I think he got embarrassed, nervous, whatever, then jumped up and left. I don't know where he was supposed to stay or who he was staying with. I think he went up to the Lodge and called for a cab, because that's what I heard. I really don't know."

"What do you think happened to Scotty regarding his injury?" West asked.

"I only know what I've been told by others," he stated. "Unless you just don't know what's going on, how do you walk off something and land on your head?"

"Have you heard any theories of foul play," Yates questioned him.

"I've heard three things," Bryant said. "I've heard John, Blake and I did it, I heard Chris York did it, and I've heard Blake did it and John and I are covering for him. I know for a fact these are some of the rumors floating around Glasgow."

Detective Yates and Sergeant West thanked Bryant for his time and then asked for his wife to join them for questioning. Bryant headed to another room of their apartment to watch their seven-year-old son.

Holli related much of the same information to police. When West got to the point of when she was awakened by her husband, he asked her if there was any type of argument between them over what had transpired between Bryant and Scotty.

"No, none," she said. "When Bryant woke me, he told me that Scotty had attempted to perform oral sex on him. I thought he was joking at first and didn't believe him." She then explained that she got out of bed and went into the living room where John and Blake were located. They again related to her the details of what had happened. She described everyone's mindset as surreal.

"No one could believe what just happened," she said.

Holli then explained that she went outside the front door of the cabin, only minutes after being awakened by Bryant.

She said, "I wanted to see if Scotty was still there; if he was alright."

She goes on to say that her husband, John, and Blake followed her outside. They continued talking about what had happened and came inside immediately thereafter.

"Why would you be concerned if Scotty was alright?" West asked.

"I don't know," she began, "I'm a nurse, and perhaps it was just a thought. I wanted to see if he was still there, as well. I didn't think anything bad had occurred; I just had the inclination to check."

"Did anyone follow Scotty out of the cabin after he propositioned your husband?" Detective Yates asked.

"No," she declared. "Bryant came directly back to bed with me. No one was angry or upset."

After an hour and a half of interviewing the Vincents, Detective Yates and Sergeant West packed up their things and headed back to Kentucky. A week later, West would find himself interviewing Blake Oliver at the office of his attorney, Tim Gillenwater, in Glasgow. After their meeting, he would surmise Blake's responses seemed calculated and deliberate.

Five

During the mid-90s, Club 141 was *the* hotspot for gay social life in Lexington, Kentucky. Among locals the name was shortened to 141. As with most popular clubs, no one arrived there too early on a Saturday night. There were other locales to prepare yourself before making your grand entrance. Getting "prepared" involved more than grooming. What it really entailed was drinking. Joe's Bar, on South Upper, served as a launching pad to 141, providing drinks to patrons who would eventually end up at the club, like a sort of social dress rehearsal.

Behind the bar, Joe himself, dispensed booze and banter, offering up stories of "the old days" in Lexington's gay scene; how every gay bar was in someone's rec room and most required a password to enter. Some folks even had gay parties at their houses, mostly held in basements so unsuspecting neighbors wouldn't raise a fuss. The chances of being caught were, at times, so great it was recommended that party-goers park their cars blocks away to quell any suspicions.

Just as kind as he could be, Joe engaged every patron as if they were budding friends, conversationally involved in the lives of his customers. Joe quietly scrutinized new attendants to the bar and welcomed them in with open arms.

The first time I met Joe I was twenty years old. As much of one's past that Joe seemed to extract from those friendly conversations, the topic of age, strangely, never came about. I never saw anyone carded or refused a drink; certainly not "new trash," as we newbies were called. Being a virgin to Joe's, I was offered a gracious handshake from the man himself upon my initial arrival.

"Pleasure to meet you. What'd'ya have?" he said.

"Amaretto sour," was my response.

Okay, I confess, at the time, beer and any type of hard liquor was not my beverage of choice. I had simple tastes. Fruity tastes actually. Amaretto sours would eventually evolve into Capecods, turning again to white wines such as Reislings and Chardonnays. But wines were still years away.

I took a chance that first night, not being of legal age, determined not only to enter Joe's but get served as well. I ended up being served my first bar drink and some interesting conversation from my new friend Joe.

Feeding me for information about my comings and goings, Joe learned that I was from Glasgow. Upon hearing this bit of trivia, he burst into an engrossing tale of time spent in Barren County from younger days.

"Glasgow. That's near those tee pee motels, ain't it?" he asked.

Joe was referring to the Wigwam Village in Cave City, about ten miles north of Glasgow. The Wigwam Village offers tourists, and some locals, a chance to, as their signs announce, "Sleep in a Wigwam!" Within a quick drive to Mammoth Cave National Park, the Wigwam Village is a novel way for a family to rest their heads on vacations to the caves. And just as the name suggests, each individual concrete motel room is in the shape of a Native American tee pee.

The concept for this bit of roadside Americana was the brainchild of Frank A. Redford. Built in 1937 the Wigwam Village that stands today was the second such site, following the construction of the original in Horse Cave, Kentucky. Each freestanding wigwam houses a bedroom complete with private bathroom. Each has a double bed and furnishings from the 1930s. And although you'll find heating, cooling and electricity in your room, telephones are nowhere to be had. This offers families a chance to distance themselves from technological distractions and enjoy the time spent together.

Of the original seven Wigwam Villages built by Redford throughout the years, only two remain intact. One stands proudly in Cave City while the other sits quietly in Holbrook, Arizona.

I explained to Joe that yes, Glasgow was, in fact, near the site of "those tee pee motels" and asked how he knew of them.

"I went to many a gatherin's there years ago, if you know what I mean," he said, pouring me another amaretto sour.

I had no idea what he meant, but nodded my head and smiled as though I were in on the secret.

Fumbling for a way to respond, in the hopes that Joe would continue his story and that I might grasp exactly what it was that he was getting at, all I could muster up was, "Uh huh."

At that point Joe turned away and headed to the far end of the bar. Three catty trolls had muscled their way towards the beer taps and Joe abandoned his discussion with me to attend to their thirsts.

I felt like all chances were now lost for Joe to elaborate on these suspicious gatherings being held on the concrete reservation. Turning towards the table where my friends were sitting, I motioned for J.D. to approach the stool next to mine at the bar.

Having already gotten pre-"prepared" before leaving his apartment on the way to Joe's, J.D. was pretty sloshed at this point, making it difficult for him to digest my instructions.

"You want me to say what?" he garbled.

"I want you to ask Joe more about the goings-on at the Wigwam Village?"

J.D. stared at me with drunken confusion. His eyes were glossy, his face was silent, and for a second I thought I had lost him completely.

"What the fuck are you talking about?"

Sighing heavily, I grabbed his shoulders and forced J.D. to hang on to every word.

"When Joe comes back," I explained, "I'm gonna tell him that you want to hear more about the things that used to happen at the Wigwam Village."

In his facial expression I could see a light was slowly brightening behind those glassy green eyes.

"Then," I continued, "I'll know what it is he's talking about without looking stupid."

I wasn't exactly sure what J.D. was about to say at that moment. Behind those eyes I could see words forming, about to project. His mouth was open. Either he still didn't understand my intentions, or, for the sake of argument, he would agree, drunk and reluctantly, so he could quickly return to the table and another round of beers.

Let me stop here and explain to the reader my reaction to the sight of vomit. I could never be a provider of healthcare, such as a doctor or nurse. I have never held back a friend's hair while they expelled a night's worth of partying into someone's toilet. I can barely watch someone spit, let alone hurl. I, myself, respond with dry heaves at the very notion that someone else might actually be getting sick. Knowing my distaste, Kory, upon occasion, will even fake throwing up just to get a rise out of me and watch me squirm. He finds it amusing. I find it repulsive.

My aversion to the sight of vomit stems from elementary school. During the middle of a lovely Friday afternoon lunch, which always consisted of tuna fish sandwiches, followed by the best fudge brownie in the history of the world, the cafeteria suddenly exploded with the screams of eight- and nine-year-olds, witnessing a sight of unbridled horrors. Too frightened to run, too aghast to look away, boys and girls stood motionless watching classmate, Wendy Asher, erupt like a once-dormant volcano holding back hundreds of years of pressure until that fateful day when earth's crust can no longer restrain the forces from within.

For what seemed like hours, Wendy expelled toffee-colored vomit, filled with bits of white bread, relish and tuna fish. Although only a lunchtime medley of digested food, the amount of puke rivaled that of an entire family's Thanksgiving Day feast. A stockpile of meals was returning violently from its host.

Wendy retched and moaned with the fervor of a possessed child, fighting demons during an exorcism. Alongside the ghastly sounds of deep, exhaustive pains, vomit poured forth like a broken human hydrant. It kept coming and coming and coming with no future end in sight. Soon, the children's worn-out screams faded as the initial revulsion subsided and expressions turned to appalled fascination as to when this episode would cease.

Sometime later, Wendy eventually stopped. Her head had fallen on the table, dead from exhaustion. Children slid gradually back into their chairs, too afraid to muffle a sound. Teachers turned back to their own, unfinished lunches, pushing away their trays towards the center of the table, unable to stomach another bite. Except for the jarring sound of wheels on a mop bucket being dragged across the cafeteria floor by the custodian, the room was silent.

I, alone, remained standing, transfixed upon the monstrous lake in the center of the room, one small tear trailing down my nine-year-old face. Feeling the terror rising, I suddenly shut my lips together tightly. And then it happened. I threw up in my own mouth.

Not wanting the school to discover my secret, afraid to start another juvenile riot in the cafeteria, praying that I would live another day after my attempt to stifle more pandemonium, I succumbed to an act of desperation. I swallowed.

. . .

Back at Joe's, J.D.'s lips were, what I thought, about to form the response I was hoping for. Instead, to my horror, J.D. threw up. In a terribly unselfish act of respect he managed to catch most all of it with cupped hands. What he managed to miss, thankfully avoiding any part of me, landed on the bar and underneath his stool.

While he stumbled off to the men's room, I dry heaved for a full minute before finally rushing outside into the fresh air. The sounds, sight, and smell of J.D.'s revulsion brought back that fateful afternoon in elementary school. Remembering that experience, I finally succumbed to my own bit of sick.

Gathering myself in the alley behind Joe's I heard a metal door opening. As I turned to the sound of broken springs I saw Joe emerging from inside. Grasping a black garbage bag, he was followed by two of the three trolls that had earlier cut short our conversation. I could tell something suspicious was afoot. One of the trolls, considerably shorter than the other, had a thick head of gray hair. His right hand was fumbling in his pants pocket, searching for something. The taller troll was more business-like, talking with his hands.

I couldn't hear what was being said, but by the sight of the tall troll's gestures, it wasn't a pleasant conversation. The shorter troll stopped digging in his pocket and pulled out a small plastic bag, forcing it into Joe's hands. Then, without speaking, the tall troll pointed his finger at Joe. That was it. The two men headed back through the door in which they came, leaving Joe holding both the small plastic bag and the garbage in both hands.

Joe turned in my direction and headed toward me, tossing the garbage bag over his left shoulder. It wasn't until he was fairly close, standing beside a dumpster, that he even noticed someone else in the alley.

"Hey kid," he said. You givin' blowjobs out here?"

I watched him toss the black bag into the receptacle and furtively stash the smaller bag into his apron pocket.

"I just needed some fresh air," I replied. "My friend got a little sick and I started feeling woozy." I wanted to know more about the secret meeting I had just witnessed, but I knew the moment was right to continue our talk about Joe's days at the Wigwam Village. I may not get the chance again.

"So you said you spent some time in Cave City," I asked.

Realizing I was bringing the conversation back to where it had previously ended, Joe nodded his head.

"I was there once or twice. Maybe three times. I had to go experience what everybody was talkin' about."

Now I had to know more. "Experience what?" I asked.

A large smirk glistened across his face. He stepped forward, leaning in close. Both hands reached out, aiming for my head. He pulled me closer. His green eyes were looking directly into mine. In his, I saw more than age. I saw years of secrets hiding behind them. Not only his secrets but also those of others who had confided in him. For a second I prayed that no one would walk by and see me in a darkened alleyway, face to face with a sixty-plus year old man whose hands were holding my head. Finally, without the melodramatic orchestration I thought should accompany his reveal, he said, "If those wigwams could talk, nobody in Barren County would be safe."

Then, just as the tall troll had ended with him, Joe pointed his finger at me. He winked. "I gotta get back inside."

Joe headed back inside the bar, leaving me standing there in the alley by myself. I was shocked, but I didn't know why. This was the first time an outsider had ever mentioned the possibility of something scandalous happening in my hometown. For twenty years I held the impression that home was as boring as a Norman Rockwell painting, and here was a total stranger accusing Glasgow of something more. I couldn't believe it. Not the fact that Glasgow had a secret, but that someone who wasn't a resident knew. I had to get to the bottom of this.

Rushing back inside through the front door I saw J.D. sitting at the table with the others as though nothing had happened. He looked normal, except for the long, thin wet spot running down the front of his grey t-shirt. I joined the table and told them what Joe had said to me in the alleyway.

"So what do you think happened?" Brian asked.

"I don't know," I replied. "But it's gotta be something pretty big for him to say what he said."

J.D. leaned in holding his beer bottle. "It's wigwams. Maybe they used to scalp people there."

Everyone's eyes rolled. Kelli chimed in. "Just go ask him. Point blank. It may not be anything. You may be blowing this all out of proportion."

I thought about it for a second. Maybe Kelli was right. Joe was in his sixties and although he seemed pretty eccentric maybe his idea of a scandal was nothing more than a young lady baring her ankles to the world.

"You're right," I said. "Here goes."

I headed back to the bar, determined to get a direct answer out of Joe. As I approached him the three trolls were making their way across the floor and beginning to exit, not before each one gave me a look up and down. I smiled, shyly, even though I was throwing up on the inside. Figuratively.

"Hey Joe," I began.

"Another drink?" he asked.

"No thanks." I started to ramble, "Look, I know we just met and everything, and I know this is still all new to me, and call me naïve, but I was just wondering if you could just tell me what it was exactly that you were talking about when you said that thing about if the wigwams could talk and how no one in Barren County would be safe." I felt like an idiot.

Without missing a beat, Joe whispered, "Sex parties."

"WHAT?!" I exclaimed. Realizing how loudly I had been, I turned around only to find most of the bar staring in my direction. Now I really felt like an idiot.

Joe laughed. "That's right. Some friends of mine invited me down there back in the day. That, of course, was the Swingin' 70s."

Things were different then, I thought to myself.

"It wasn't so different from today," he added. "You know how it is."

I had no idea how it was.

"So what exactly went on?" I pressed for more details.

"Sex mostly. And drugs. The first time I was ever there I walked in to one of them rooms and saw about ten people doin' it."

I had seen the inside of those motel rooms and I just couldn't believe you could possibly fit more than four or five people in there. I imagined these slippery, writhing bodies, naked and sweaty, cramped inside the room, rising and falling as if trying to free themselves from the confined space.

"Were women there?" I had to know.

"Yeah, a few. It was men and women, men and men, women and women. Nobody seemed to care. The third time I went no women showed up. That was the last time I was there and the best time I was there. Watched a guy snort coke off a city councilman's hard-on."

I was stunned. It sure beat bare ankles. Joe continued the story, telling me more than I thought I wanted to know. He said everyone was fairly safe, using condoms even at a time when most sex was bareback. The drugs of choice were pot and poppers although cocaine and PCP made their appearances. He went on, in vivid detail, describing every body, every position, leaving nothing out. The kicker was the mention of notable locals, such as elected officials, married church deacons partaking without their wives, and other fine, upstanding pillars of the community that were held with moral respect in the eyes of the town. I was speechless and wishing I had never asked.

I headed back to my table where everyone's eyes fell upon me. I could see the look of anticipation in their expressions. They appeared to have been sitting silently, waiting for my return to tell of the big reveal. I stood there staring back until Kelli finally broke the tension.

"Well, what did he say?" she asked.

I cleared my throat, then said nothing.

J.D. spoke up, "We're waiting."

I took a deep breath. "Kelli was right," I exhaled. "He started going on about gambling and poker. It was nothing. Nothing."

The group turned back to their drinks and started chatting again as if there had been no interruption. I stood there another few seconds, watching them, before I sat back down and joined in their conversation. These were my best friends, but for some reason I couldn't tell them what Joe had said. A sense of shame had come over me. I had the urge to protect my hometown; to keep others in the dark who were proud of Glasgow, and therefore promised myself never to tell anyone what I had heard. However, an hour and several drinks later would change all that, and Scotty would be the person to whom I eventually spilled my guts.

By 11:00 p.m. it was socially acceptable to show up at 141. We left our table at Joe's to gather around yet another table in the rear of the club. A line had formed outside the entrance with more groups that knew the unspoken protocol of going out. I was regretting not going to the bathroom before leaving the bar and was hopping around in place in an effort to subside my bladder pains.

J.D., annoyed with my antics, snapped, "You're gonna get us kicked out before we even get in!"

"I have to pee!" I shot back. "Besides, Miss Delaney is working the door."

The Lady Delaney, aka Billy Thomas, was a regular performer at Club 141. On nights he wasn't entertaining the crowds, he was helping out by being the doorman, or doorwoman if he was in drag. We knew each other through mutual friends, and since he had a crush on me, I used it to my advantage to gain entrance to the club.

Billy would scrutinize everyone's IDs before allowing them inside. He would stare intently at the photo on the card and then examine the person up and down with his eyes, even if he knew them. The only person with whom he didn't perform this little ritual was me. He would just stare at me, up and down, leaving out the ID part.

The line was moving especially slow, and I wasn't sure how long I was going to make it. I contemplated rushing back over to Joe's for relief.

J.D. yelled out, "Tell that queen to step on it!" The people standing in front of us turned in our direction.

"Oh," I said, "you're worried *I'm* gonna get us kicked out of here!?" I continued hopping.

Billy heard J.D.'s remark and jokingly shot back, "Bitch, don't make me take off my heels and beat your ass in front of all these people!" The crowd laughed.

"You're gonna get us in trouble," I told him.

"Trouble is not much fun unless it finds you first," J.D. replied, "Besides, that CQ is in love with you."

Billy had a very thick, Kentucky twang to his voice and the term, CQ, was used to refer to a gay man that talked as such and behaved like a "good ole boy." These guys generally live in outlying towns like Richmond or Frankfort, but drive to Lexington on weekends and let loose at the bars.

During the week, they work at nurseries potting bulbs or sell paint and window treatments at Home Depot; jobs that satisfy their queer longings to be florists and interior decorators without compromising their expected roles of manhood. CQ stands for Country Queer. I admit I have dated a few.

At this point I decided to jump out of line and rush back to Joe's to use the restroom. Turning the corner on South Upper, my pains began to intensify. I was running with my knees crossed and clenching my teeth in agony, yet I still had hope I was going to make it. I burst through the entrance door and scurried to the back of the bar towards the restrooms. Two girls were already waiting to go in.

"Oh God!" I yelled. The girls turned toward me, eyebrows furled.

"Are you alright?" one asked. "You don't look good."

I was wincing. "I have to peeeeeee!"

The girl stepped aside and motioned with her right hand towards the bathroom door. "Go ahead."

I reached out to turn the knob when the door opened. Standing before me was Scotty, wearing a white polo shirt and blue baseball cap from the Gap. In unison we exclaimed, "What are *you* doing here?!"

I grabbed his arm and pulled him out of my way. "I have to pee!" Slamming the door behind me, I yelled back, "Wait for me!"

I remained in the restroom for five minutes. When I emerged, I was completely relieved and had to sit down out of exhaustion. The two girls were gone. Scotty joined me at the table.

"So how'd you get in here," I asked him.

"Fake," he said, holding up his wallet. "Just got it last week."

I looked around the room. "Who are you here with?"

"James and a couple of his friends from Berea," he said.

James Wallace was Scotty's roommate and someone whom I had a big crush on as well. I had seen James around campus many times before I ever knew that he and Scotty shared an apartment. The day I finally found out, I was actually visiting Scotty for the first time when James walked out of his bedroom. I was totally caught off guard and too nervous to say anything. When he left, I screamed and giggled like a schoolgirl, begging Scotty to set me up with him. At the time, however, he was dating someone else. Years later I would occasionally run into him at the bars in Chicago where he, too, was residing. Sadly, the last time I saw him we were discussing Scotty's recent death. I haven't seen him since.

I glanced at my watch. "You guys should come over to 141," I suggested.

"We were just about to head over there," he said. "Natalie Gaye's performing tonight, and I can't miss that!"

"I haven't seen a drag show in ages," I admitted.

Scotty snapped, "Then you're missing out."

I shook my head. "No, I'm not. I'm always afraid they're gonna pick me out of the crowd and embarrass me. I'd rather be dancing. Or drinking."

Scotty smirked, "I know what you'd rather be doing." He was motioning to the other table with his eyes.

"I thought he was dating someone," I asked.

"He is," Scotty said. "The guy in the black shirt."

I turned around to see a tall blonde with his arm around James. At that same moment both men looked up and in my direction. I had been caught staring.

"Thanks a lot," I said, rolling my eyes at Scotty.

"You're welcome," he said.

"Oh my gosh I forgot to tell you something," I began. And then I stopped.

Scotty leaned towards me with great enthusiasm, "What?"

My head began working overtime, trying to save myself from telling Scotty the news I had heard earlier from Joe. I was frozen, mouth agape, waiting for any words to fall out. None were coming.

"Are you gonna tell me," he asked again.

One word formed. "I." And then I stopped again. I really needed to work on my improvisation skills.

Scotty was staring at me, patiently waiting for my story. And then it hit me.

"Oh, nevermind. I was gonna tell you about somebody who just came out, but I remembered you don't even know him. I was thinking about someone else. Sorry."

Not seeming to mind, Scotty started in with his own bit of gossip. "Speaking of which," he began, "do you remember a guy who went to Barren County high school named Chris Carter?"

I wasn't familiar with any students who went to the county schools. "Nope, sorry," I said.

"Oh, it doesn't matter. Big queen." Scotty laughed.

I looked at my watch again, realizing I had left my friends in line. I was sure they were inside the club by now and decided to return.

"I gotta get back. I'll see you all over there," I said.

Scotty stood up and headed over to the table with James and his friends. "Later," he yelled back.

When I turned the corner towards 141, I noticed that none of my friends were in line anymore. In fact, there was no line, just Billy sitting on a stool, filing his nails.

"Hey sweetie!" he shouted. "Why'd you run off a minute ago? I was waiting for you."

"I had to go to the little boy's room," I said. "Badly."

Billy grabbed my arm and pulled me towards him.

"I would have let you go on inside if you'd told me. All you had to do was ask," he said. "Nicely."

I sighed. "Now you tell me."

He then grabbed my right hand in his and carefully stamped it with black ink. The stamp read, "SLUT."

"Classy," I told him.

He started to reach in his pocket. "I have "WHORE" if you'd rather," he said.

"SLUT's fine, thanks," I said, trying to retrieve my arm from his grip. He wasn't letting it go.

"So when are you gonna go out with me?" he asked.

"When you get a real job," I shot back. He slapped my hand. I had no intention of ever dating Billy, but I didn't see the harm in flirting with him. He was a very sincere person and I appreciated that.

"Bitch!" he said.

Just then I noticed Scotty, James, and the group walking around the corner, headed in my direction. Billy apparently recognized James.

"We don't allow trash in our establishment," he remarked.

James laughed, saying, "Obviously they take the trash out if you're sittin' here!"

While the others giggled, Billy and James air kissed each other's cheeks.

"I need to see ID's, boys," Billy announced.

Each person in the group slowly went through the thorough examination process from Billy. Scotty looked nervous and held back until the rest of the guys had been inspected.

"You're next, sweetie," Billy told Scotty.

As if in slow motion, Scotty handed off his fake ID. Billy took a quick look at the laminated card and then stared into Scotty's eyes. Another peek at the card, then a longer gaze at Scotty's face. I could tell he was anxious.

"I can vouch for this one," I interjected. "He's a fellow Glaswegian."

Billy turned towards me. "A what?!"

"We're both from Glasgow," I explained.

Billy looked at Scotty and then turned back to me. "Good Lord, what's in the water down there?!" he said, giving Scotty's hand a stamp.

If he only knew, I thought to myself. Motioning for Scotty to follow me inside, I said goodbye to Billy. "We'll see you later Miss Delaney." Then I blew him a kiss.

"Thanks for that," Scotty whispered to me. "I thought I had been found out for a second."

"He does that to everybody. I was just trying to hurry him along," I said. The two of us walked up the steps to the main floor and looked around to see who was there. I also started searching for J.D. and the others.

Scotty seemed to be deep in thought. "There are a lot of us from Glasgow," he said.

"A lot of what?" I asked him.

"Gays," he answered.

"Of course," I said. "I can name ten without thinking."

Scotty laughed. "I'm sure there's a couple of new ones you don't know about it."

"I'm sure," I said. "I'm proud to say I've never dated any of them though." We both looked at each as if knowing what the other one was thinking.

After a few, silent seconds Scotty spoke up. "You said 'dated,' right?"

"Yep," I laughed.

"Yeah, me neither," he replied, smirking.

Just then I viewed J.D. stumbling from one of the bars on the main floor. He seemed to be headed upstairs. I turned to Scotty.

"I'm gonna catch up with my friends," I said. "I'll see you later."

Upstairs I found the rest of my group, sitting at a table overlooking the dance floor. A waitress came by, and I ordered another amaretto sour. Kelli ordered shots for all of us. While waiting for the drinks I scanned the room, looking for cute guys. There were dozens of people dancing to a remix of Billie Ray Martin's "Your Loving Arms." Scotty was among them. I also noticed James and his blond, dancing closely together.

"I wish they'd play something good!" J.D. shouted over the music. He lit a cigarette and threw the matches in the center of the table.

Over a loud speaker, a voice rang out. "Ladies and ladies, tonight's performances by Miss Maya Monroe and Miss Natalie Gaye will begin in five minutes. We ask that you please clear the dance floor now." The music continued.

I looked over at J.D. I knew he hated drag shows more than I did but loved to make fun of the performers.

"Don't they have another room for these tired old queens?" he snapped.

Our waitress showed up at that moment with a tray full of drinks.

"Thank God," J.D. said. "I'm gonna need it now!"

We each grabbed a shot glass and toasted to the booze. Down our throats they went.

"SHIT!" Brian yelled. "What the hell was that?!"

"Buttery nipples," Kelli said. "I told you that already."

Brian looked sick. "I thought we decided on tequila."

Kelli shook her head. "We changed our minds when you were in the bathroom."

Brian flagged down our waitress and ordered everyone but Kelli a tequila shot. I could already sense I was going to have a hangover the next morning. Then I heard the dance music getting quieter. The lights and lasers started to fade. Most of the people had left the dance floor and were standing around its perimeter. The voice from the loud speaker returned.

"Good evening everyone!" it said. "Please welcome to the stage tonight's first performer, Miss Maya Monroe!"

The crowd screamed and cheered as a loud bass began to thump. Imitating the beat, everyone started to clap to the rhythm. A single spot light ignited and standing in the center stood a six-foot tall female impersonator with a bright red updo wig and long, flowing black gown. Channeling Reba McEntire, Maya began singing "Fancy," a crowd favorite.

"What queen *hasn't* done this song," J.D. cracked.

Maya strolled around the dance floor, lip-syncing the words to the song with over- exaggerated head and arm movements. The crowd below was loving it and many were offering Maya folded bills for kisses. She refused no one.

By the end of the number our second set of shots and first set of tequila arrived. J.D. and Brian didn't bother toasting this time. They quickly grabbed a glass from the tray and downed the drink. The rest of us prepped ourselves with salt and followed the shot with lemon. I winced. I hated tequila but loved the fact it would get me drunk faster.

"Chug that girlie drink, Troxall," J.D. shouted.

I reached for my amaretto sour and sipped. Just then I spotted Scotty coming up the stairs. He saw me, and I waved him over.

"Natalie's up next," he said, sitting next to me.

"Alright everybody." The voice was back. "Let's give another round of applause to Maya Monroe." The crowd clapped again. "Now please welcome to the floor our very own Miss Natalie Gaye!" More applause.

Just then, a full-figured Natalie Gaye emerged from behind a curtain wearing a Pucci-inspired dress and giant white afro. She started to sing "I Need a Man" by Grace Jones. The crowd went crazy. I guzzled my drink.

"Go get us more booze," I told J.D. "No one's at the bar."

"Gladly," he said, walking away from the table.

I turned to Scotty. "He's not a big drag fan," I explained.

"Let's go down there and give her a dollar," he suggested.

I shook my head. "Have fun without me."

Scotty looked disappointed. "Oh come on!" he said.

I was not about to leave my seat and give away good money that could go towards alcohol. "You can go down there," I started to say, "or stay up here and listen to the little gem I heard earlier about Glasgow." I was beginning to feel the effects of the two shots.

"How 'bout I run down there with my dollar, then run back up here?" he asked.

"No dice," I answered.

Scotty remained seated next to me while I told him the story that Joe had offered up. I mentioned the wigwams, the sex, the drugs, and the list of names that I had been told. And although my head was swimming slightly, I left out no details. When I was finished, Scotty asked me one question. "Do you believe him?"

I don't remember my response, but I felt, deep down, that there was truth in what I had heard. I had no reason not to believe him. But what I remember most from that conversation was that my story did not seem to faze Scotty the way I thought it would. He appeared neither shocked nor particularly interested the way I, myself, had previously reacted. To this day I wonder if he ever told anyone else.

As the night wore on, Scotty joined his roommate and their friends on the dance floor. I remained at the table with J.D. and the others until we grew tired of the scene. I left 141 that night without saying goodbye to anyone.

It wasn't until much later, while lying in bed, reflecting on Joe's tale, that it truly dawned on me. He had been talking about my hometown. This wasn't New York or Los Angeles or some seedy European location you only see in a movie. This was real. And for the first time in my life I felt a bit deceived by Glasgow. It had suddenly lost its squeaky clean image that I grew up believing. Little did I know that this wouldn't be the last time Glasgow would betray me.

Six

On the afternoon of July 14th, Detective West met with Blake Oliver. During the interview West noted that Blake was apparently nervous and seemed much more reluctant to speak than other witnesses. It was obvious to the Sergeant that Blake was not going to volunteer any information.

"Did you rent Cabin 507," West asked Blake.

"No," Blake answered. "John Dickinson paid for it."

"It's on record that you rented it," West explained.

"No, it was John," he stated.

West said, "There's a notation on the room invoice that you paid using a gift certificate."

"No," he said again, "the gift certificate belonged to John."

West reviewed with Blake those staying at the cabin that night, clarifying their names. Blake appeared tense. After going over these things with him, West paused and told him to relax.

"It was obvious to me that he was extremely nervous," West later explained. "He was reluctant to tell me anything he was not prompted to answer. He seemed to have to think about every answer he gave me, even with regard to verifying people he knew to be at the cabin. His demeanor was totally apart from what I had experienced in speaking with him over the phone and far from cooperative."

West told Blake and his attorney, "You're a witness in this case. You're also a person of interest simply due to the fact, by your own admission, that you were one of the last people to see Scotty."

The Sergeant went on to explain that if he knew he did not have anything to do with Scotty's injuries, he could relax.

Blake responded, "I want to cooperate with you in any way I can. I've undergone over six weeks of viscous rumors, and it's very stressful."

"I'm just trying to find the facts," West stated.

West began again by asking Blake about the time everyone was gathering at the cabin. He further made the comment that it was normal in situations like these that people would gather after such an event, like a reunion.

Gillenwater interrupted, saying, "I'm not going to let my client get into the sociological observations of what most people do at a party."

West was quiet. Blake's attorney smiled, "Hey, I gotta earn my money…make you earn yours."

"How many people were at the cabin," West asked Blake.

"I don't know," he said, "around thirty."

"And when did Mark Nelson and Angelo Pedicini leave?"

"I'm not sure about Nelson, but Pedicini left around 3:30 a.m.," he said.

West then asked Blake questions aimed at narrowing the time frame to when he, Bryant, John, and Scotty were the only ones up and in the cabin. He asked him what Scotty was doing during that time.

"Was he interacting, talking…" West began.

Blake replied, "His interactions were very minimal."

Once again, Blake's attorney interrupted. "I don't want to get into all this scandalous stuff or anything that has the potential to be scandalous. Blake can tell you that Scotty made a pass at Bryant Vincent, but I'm not gonna let it go any further."

West asked, "Did Scotty make a pass at *you*?"

Blake nodded. "Yes," he said.

"Did it surprise you?"

"Yeah," he said, nodding again.

West then asked, "Did anyone there know Scotty was a homosexual?"

This time Mr. Gillenwater interrupted, saying he wanted to take a time out to confer with his client. West was simply attempting to get to the issue of how Blake, John, and Bryant reacted to Scotty's sexual advances.

When the three men reconvened, West again asked Blake how he responded to the pass that Scotty had made. After some hesitation, Blake cautiously stated that he laughed.

"I said, 'No thanks, I'll be alright,'" Blake told the officer.

"What was his response? Did Scotty say anything?" West asked. "I'm trying to understand what Scotty might have been thinking?"

With Mr. Gillenwater's input, Blake said, "I didn't get a feel for what Scotty was thinking."

"Did you tell anyone about this at the party?" West asked.

Blake said, "Yeah, and no one believed me."

West asked, "Did anyone get mad or upset?"

"Absolutely not," Blake said.

"And when did this occur?" West asked.

"I don't know. 3:30 a.m. or 4:00 a.m. I wasn't wearing a watch."

"I don't want you to get hung up on the time at the sacrifice of the information," West explained. "Did Scotty stay at the cabin after the pass?"

"No," said Blake, "he immediately got up and left."

West began asking Blake about his past relationship with Scotty. He explained to the Sergeant that it had been ten years since he had seen Scotty and that Scotty wasn't in their social group while in high school.

Sergeant West then asked Blake about the sexual advance Scotty allegedly made at Bryant Vincent. Blake described Scotty as getting up from the kitchen chair, walking past him, on the couch, and kneeling down next to Bryant, who was on an adjacent couch. Again, Mr. Gillenwater interrupted the interview, stating he was going to stop Blake at that point unless it was going to be material to the investigation. West explained to Gillenwater that it may or may not establish a motive for Bryant to hurt

Scotty, rather than his client.

"Mr. Vincent was an athlete," West explained to the attorney. "*IS* an athlete. And seems to be the antithesis of what Scotty was as a person. Scotty was in the band, Vincent was a jock. It's reasonable to say the typical male response might very well be anger. This would especially be dependent on the level of the proposition. I just want Blake's statement regarding this specific incident."

After West explained his position, Mr. Gillenwater again asked to confer with his client. The Sergeant stopped the interview until the client and his attorney could speak privately.

When Blake returned, he told West that he was uncomfortable talking about details of interactions between Scotty and Bryant because of the assumption West had made earlier.

"You assumed a stereotypical response because Bryant was an athlete. And because of that, you assumed his response was anger. That couldn't be further from the truth," Blake said.

"That's what I wanted to know," West stated. "Can you characterize Bryant's response?"

Blake explained, "Bryant said, 'Ho…hold up. I'm not going to do this unless you all are going to do this.'"

"And what did John say?" West asked.

Blake replied, "John said 'Fuck this, I'm outta here,' and he left the room. Then Bryant looked back at me and said, 'What about you?' I said, 'Hell no, I've already been through this once tonight.' As soon as I said that, Scotty got up and left the room."

West asked Blake if the incident when Scotty propositioned Bryant occurred after he had propositioned him? He affirmed that to be the proper sequence of events. He went on to say that Scotty propositioned him, left the cabin, then came back when he, John, Bryant, and Angelo were on the porch.

"How long was Scotty gone?" West asked.

"I don't know," Blake answered. "Long enough for me to get up, go across the room and tell Stacey and Andrew McChord and Ellody

Dickinson what had occurred. They all laughed and didn't believe me. I told them I wasn't sleeping on that couch after that occurred."

"Did anyone follow Scotty when he left?" West asked Blake.

"I'm not aware of anyone leaving the cabin," Blake said. "The only person to have left during that time frame was Scotty."

West asked, "What did you and the others do after Scotty left the cabin the last time?"

Blake explained, "I spent some time speaking to Bryant and Holli until they went to bed. John and I talked to Ellody briefly, talked some more to each other, then cleaned up the cabin. John told me he was tired, and I told him I was going home to sleep."

"What time was this?" West asked.

"I don't know," Blake said, "but the sun was up at that point. We walked out to my truck and exchanged a refrigerator into John's vehicle. Then I left."

West digressed back to the time Holli Vincent got out of bed. Blake had said Holli was in bed at the time of Scotty's sexual advance.

"What do you think awakened her?" West asked Blake.

Blake replied, "I assumed she heard them talking after Scotty left and realized Bryant wasn't in bed with her."

Blake recalled that Bryant explained to Holli what Scotty had done. He said her response was shock. West asked Blake if he remembered her walking outside. He told him he could not recall that. Blake ended the interview by saying that neither he nor John said anything to Holli.

"She's not *our* wife," Blake told West.

. . .

The next day Sergeant West met Scotty's mother. This was the first contact he had made with her in reference to the investigation. He updated her on the status of the case and asked to retrieve Scotty's cellphone. The rangers had given it to Brandi, who in turn gave it to her mother. West noted that the silver Nokia phone was inside a clear plastic sandwich bag and appeared clean and new. Scotty's mother explained that she and her daughter had used it on several occasions days after her son's injuries at the Lodge, but West assured her he was only interested to see data around the time frame Scotty was at the reunion. He marked the phone Exhibit #5.

On Friday, July 16th, Detective Pickett had a brief interview with Amy Claywell Sawyer.

"Can you explain your relation to Scotty?" Pickett asked.

"Scotty's sister, Brandi, was married to my brother," she explained.

"And you drove Scotty to his reunion?" Pickett inquired.

Sawyer responded, "Yes. Scotty didn't own a car at that time. He called me at work the day of the reunion and asked if I would take him there."

Pickett asked, "What did you say?"

"I told him I didn't get off until 7:15 p.m. or 7:30 p.m. He said that was fine and to pick him up afterwards."

"Did you drive straight there?" West asked.

"After we left his house, we stopped by the liquor store," she said. "He purchased a six-pack of beer or wine coolers, I think."

Sawyer explained that Scotty was excited about going to the reunion and talked about seeing Blake Haines and Anne Gentry. She told the detective that the conversation was of a general nature.

"We arrived between 8:00 p.m. and 8:15 p.m.," she said. "He told me that he had his cellphone and would probably catch a ride with Stacy Renfro Phillips because she lived in Bowling Green too. He told me that, if he stayed the night, he would call me the next morning. He mentioned calling a cab, but they had earlier quoted him a $40 fee to take him to the Lodge. He thanked me for the ride, and that was the last time I saw him or talked to him."

Pickett asked Sawyer to describe Scotty's mental state or a possible drug habit. She stated that she never saw him depressed. She said that he did not have a drug habit but did use cocaine socially by his own admission. Sawyer ended the interview by saying Scotty was one of the happiest people she ever knew.

Later that day Detective Pickett paid a visit to the Lodge to speak with Ranger Adwell. The two men entered the Ranger's office, then Adwell shut the door.

"Is there any new information in the Martin case?" Adwell asked.

Pickett explained, "Sergeant West is the lead officer. You'll need to speak to him about the status of the case. However, the case has not reached a conclusion and there's more investigation needed."

"I just want to help in any way I can," Adwell said.

"Just answer all questions truthfully," Pickett answered, "and if you omitted anything to let Sergeant West know."

Adwell added, "Lawyers with the Parks Department call me at least weekly and sometimes more. They want to know if I have copies of reports and what has happened."

"Just refer them to West," Pickett advised.

"Alright," Adwell said.

Pickett told the Ranger that there had been some questions as to Ranger Hogue having some notes on the case, still in his possession that KSP had not seen.

"I've been told that those are his personal notes," Adwell said, "and that he didn't think there was any reason for turning those over."

"Why don't you talk to him again," Pickett suggested, "and make sure there isn't anything in there that we could use, no matter how minor."

Adwell concluded by telling the detective that he would talk to his ranger.

The next week Detective Pickett and Sergeant West arrived at the residence of Stacy Renfro Phillips to speak with her about the events of the reunion. She confirmed to the officers that she and Scotty had been classmates and friends.

She explained to them that Scotty had invited her over for dinner the week before the reunion. "We talked about going and seeing people we haven't seen for a while," she said.

"When did you first see him that night," West asked.

"I didn't see him until after the dinner," she explained. "I was standing outside when I noticed him getting out of a car. He was wearing a blue shirt, black pants, and had a shoulder strap bag on."

Pickett asked, "What happened during the reunion?"

"Everyone there was having a good time without any conflict," she began. "When the band quit playing around midnight, several people decided to go to one of the cabins for an after party. Scotty and I talked about getting back home to Bowling Green. My ride had already left and Scotty didn't have one, so we decided to stay a while and split a cab if necessary."

"Then what happened at the cabins?" West asked.

"Well when I arrived at the cabin, there were probably thirty or forty people already there, including Scotty. He was sitting on the porch with some other people."

"Were people drinking?" Pickett inquired.

Stacy replied, "Yeah, and someone even gave me a drink when I showed up." She paused. "At some point I went inside to use the bathroom. When I was in there someone knocked on the door. Then Scotty said, 'It's me, I'm coming in.'"

"What did you do?" West asked.

"I told him to wait a minute," she said, "and he did. Then he came in and said, 'Do you wanna do something?'"

Stacy explained to the officers that she didn't know what it was. "He pulled out a vial from his fanny pack and asked me if I wanted some. I told him no and asked what he was doing with it."

Pickett asked, "What did he do with it?"

"He snorted it and left the bathroom," she said.

She went on to say that she received a ride from a friend who drove her to her parents' home in Glasgow. "I told him I was ready to leave, but Scotty said he was enjoying himself and wanted to stay. That's the last time I saw him."

. . .

On July 21st, Detective Pickett met with Sheriff's Deputy Steve Runyon to review his actions that took place the day Scotty was discovered behind the Lodge.

"On May 30th," Runyon began, "I was advised about an incident down at the Barren River State Park. I spoke to Ranger Adwell and told him he needed to investigate it himself, due to the fact it occurred at the Park. He told me they didn't want them investigating something that serious, so eventually I told him I'd at least help him out."

Deputy Runyon described meeting with Rangers Adwell and Hogue at the Park that same day. He instructed them to take photos, notes, and measure the surroundings within the loading dock area. "We measured the height of the dock and the distance from the building and wall to the point of impact," Runyon explained.

"Several photos were taken," he said, "and a photo of my portable radio was used to give an approximate location of where Mr. Martin's glasses were found. There was also a piece of chewing gum found lying on the dock floor which I photographed and advised Ranger Hogue to collect. I also took a photo of a small grassy area that appeared to have been walked on."

. . .

On Sunday, July 25th, Sergeant West attended the polygraph examination of Bryant Vincent in Bowling Green. Questions had been formulated prior to their meeting and Bryant was briefed about the required protocols with regard to the administration of the polygraph. John Bruner, a Kentucky State Police Polygraph Examiner, conducted the exam.

"Did you chase that man outside?" Mr. Bruner asked.

"No," Bryant answered. The polygraph indicated deception on this question.

Mr. Bruner continued. "Did you cause any of those injuries to that man?"

Bryant replied no. The polygraph indicated no deception.

"Did you see that man fall from the loading dock?"

"No," said Bryant. Again, no deception.

Finally Mr. Bruner asked, "Are you withholding any important information about that man's fall?"

"No," Bryant answered again. Once more, there was no deception indicated.

After the exam, Mr. Bruner explained that, for official purposes, if deception is shown on any one question of the polygraph, the whole examination is considered as a failure or showing deception. When West confronted Bryant about the fact that he showed deception with regard to chasing Scotty, Bryant was unwavering in his position that he did not chase him at all.

He maintained his assertion that he had no altercation or negative words with Scotty over his sexual advances. Bryant did, however, contradict his earlier statement in which he explained that Scotty had asked him if he could give him a blowjob. During this interview, he denied Scotty asked him that.

West then challenged Bryant with the statement Holli had made about venturing outside the cabin, after being awakened once Scotty had gone. Bryant claimed he had forgotten about that.

"Someone knocked on the door about a minute after Scotty left," he told West.

The Sergeant pointed out that this was the first instance of anyone telling him about a knock on the cabin door. None of the other witnesses had reported this.

"Would you clarify that issue," West asked, "because I haven't heard that from anybody else."

Bryant told the officer, "John Dickinson went to the door and opened it, didn't see anyone there and closed it again. Then Holli and I went to bed after that."

Again, West noted, John's statements never included such

information. Afterwards, West concluded, "It is apparent that Vincent is not telling the truth with regard to what occurred inside the cabin. Even so, there is no independent witness statements or evidence to show that he did chase Martin. There is certainly no physical evidence that Martin was assaulted prior to leaving the cabin, nor any circumstantial evidence to support the notion that Bryant Vincent had any involvement in an assault."

On the 26th, West received the final report from the medical examiner's office in Tennessee. In reviewing the Narrative Summary of Circumstances Surrounding Death, West noted nearly the entire description of circumstances were incorrect. It read, "The decedent is a 28-year-old man that was reportedly at a ten-year class reunion that was being held on a barge in Bowling Green, Kentucky, when he fell overboard and fell approximately thirty feet on 05/30/2004. The decedent sustained closed head injuries and was transported to Vanderbilt Medical Center. The decedent's condition continued to deteriorate until expiration occurred. The decedent was transported to the M.E.O. for further investigation. Sherrie L. Saint, Investigator."

West contacted and spoke with Fran Wheatley, an investigator with the department. She explained that the summary was not in need of change on their report. They simply write down the preliminary information as it is given by whomever reports it. The central focus of their report is the autopsy results and cause and manner of death, which is contingent upon West's findings.

He also addressed some minor contusions not mentioned by Dr. Levy to Detective Childers during the autopsy or in their first draft. Dr. Levy indicated that there were two ¾-inch green/yellow-colored contusions on the left side of Scotty's chest and five such contusions on his right side. Also found was a ¼-inch linear contusion on the anterior of the left ankle. Dr. Levy would advise him that those marks were not related to any sort of assault. His final summary would state, "The pattern of injuries is consistent with a moving head striking a non-moving object, for example, a fall. In my opinion, the person died as a result of the blunt force injuries to the head. The manner of death is accident."

. . .

On July 29th, West phoned and interviewed Angelo Pedicini. He confirmed he attended the reunion and described the events of the night. Sergeant West directed his questions towards what he knew about Scotty making advances towards others during the time he was at Cabin 507.

"Blake went inside the cabin at one point," Angelo said. "Then Scotty went in behind him. About five minutes later, Scotty came out and walked past us toward the Lodge. Then Blake came back out and told us all that Scotty had offered him oral sex."

"Were you surprised?" West asked.

"Yeah," he said, "Everyone was."

Angelo said he was still in the area when Scotty returned. He eventually retired to his own cabin between 3:00 a.m. and 4:00 a.m. "The only other ones awake when I left were Blake, John, Bryant, and Scotty," he explained.

"When did you find out something had happened to Scotty?" West asked.

"The next morning," Angelo began, "David and Taylor woke us up and told us about Scotty's injuries. We got dressed and went to the loading dock. I saw a pool of blood around the concrete chock block at the bottom of the hill."

West asked, "What happened next?"

Angelo said that he and others headed to the Lodge where they tried to contact Scotty's family. He recalled running into Chris York as they were walking back to their own cabin. He and Mark Nelson spoke with Chris about Scotty's injuries, then Chris mentioned the sexual advance made by Scotty toward Bryant.

"I remember seeing John and Ellody Dickinson," he said, "Stacey and Andrew McChord, and Chris. Blake and Bryant were gone by that time."

The following week, Sergeant West tried contacting Scotty's physician, John Morris, MD, who attended Scotty when he was first admitted to the trauma unit. He was looking to find information regarding a toxicology report, as he was told that none was performed. According to a spokesperson, the hospital only runs one if they feel it is medically necessary based upon the information they have at the time or if their medical protocol calls for it. In this instance, neither criteria was met, therefore no toxicology report was ever performed on Scotty.

Within the next few days Sergeant West received two bits of information he had been waiting for. The first was the medical examiner's draft. In it, Dr. Levy confirmed blunt force injuries of the head and reported that, "the pattern of the injuries is consistent with a moving head striking a non-moving object, for example, a fall. In my opinion, this person died as a result of the blunt force injuries to the head. The manner of death is pending police investigation."

Secondly, the Sergeant received a copy of the lab results from the Western Kentucky Regional Lab regarding the controlled substance found inside Scotty's bag. According to the lab report, the substance was found to be meth.

. . .

On September 3rd, Sergeant West arrived at the State Park for a scheduled interview with Ranger Adwell. Prior to their meeting, West made a final review of the loading dock, cabins, and payphone area at the Lodge. He wanted to ensure nothing had been overlooked.

"In looking over the loading dock area," he said, "I noted no significant changes with regard to the structure, or lighting, had been made. I looked at the lights on both sides of the retaining wall at the bottom of the dock. It appeared that they were still inoperable. The light protective casing and area surrounding each of them was covered in dirt and cobwebs."

He walked back to the area on top of the retaining wall, near the air conditioning units from which Scotty allegedly fell. "I noted it is readily apparent and plausible that one could fall from this area, attempting to negotiate it during daylight hours, much more so in relative darkness."

At 7:00 p.m., West met Ranger Adwell inside the Lodge.

"With regard to the scene," West asked, "at what time was it secured and how was it secured?"

Adwell indicated that the scene was secured around 9:00 a.m. He told West that he taped off the area as Deputy Runyon and Ranger Hogue took photographs and collected evidence.

West asked, "And when was that scene released?"

"On Tuesday, June 1 at approximately 9:00 a.m.," Adwell explained. "Trooper John Holbrook came out to assist us. He told us we could take down the yellow tape after we had surveyed the scene again and didn't note any further evidence to be collected."

"Did you turn over all the evidence you collected or was there anything else you discovered later which might have had evidentiary value?" West inquired.

"To my knowledge, we turned over everything." Adwell said.

West asked him about an entry made on a KSP Property Form in which property was released to the family.

"Hogue released Martin's wallet and cellphone to his sister, Brandi," he explained.

"And what about this note regarding someone picking on Scotty during the reunion?" West asked.

Adwell answered, "Deptuy Runyon told me that information during the initial investigation. He didn't say who told him that." West noted that, during the interviews with witnesses, none of them ever mentioned that anyone was picking on Scotty.

"Over the course of the investigation," West began explaining, "some family members asked me if Martin had an ice pack on his head when he was discovered. I had never gotten that indication from any of the medical personnel on the scene. Have you heard anything about that?"

No," Adwell answered. "The only thing I could surmise is that someone could have mistaken his fanny pack, which was reported to be up around his head and neck area when he was discovered."

West asked the ranger about his comment to Detective Pickett regarding other investigative notes Ranger Hogue was allegedly in possession of concerning this case. Contrary to what Pickett reported to West, Adwell stated that Hogue had, in fact, turned over all of his notes. In fact, there were photocopies that were turned over to West.

The two men then reviewed Ranger Adwell's patrol logs for further information. At 0100 to 0150 hours, Adwell noted he locked the Lodge. From 0335 to 0440 he noted, "patrol park." He told West there were seven to ten people gathered in the area in front of Cabin 507 at that time. He did not indicate anything significant, other than the people standing around. During this hour and five minute patrol, West noted, it would not be a huge divergence from witness statements regarding their activities around the cabin during that time frame. The additional hours list when Adwell was called in and began his investigation.

A note at the top of his patrol log was a weather entry for Sunday, May 30th. "Cloudy, low in 60's, light rain at 4:00 a.m." The following evening he had written, "Severe storm warning, 10:45 p.m." This corroborated statements by others with regard to the weather that weekend. It also served to support comments in Trooper Holbrook's report, indicating that by the time he met with rangers to assist them, much of the blood had been dissipated by heavy rains in the area.

...

Finally, on September 7th, Sergeant West would conclude his investigation by summarizing what he had discovered over the course of the past three months. "John Dickinson, Christopher York, Bryant and Holli Vincent, and Blake Oliver have all been interviewed in this case", he stated. "Dickinson, York, and Oliver retained counsel prior to being interviewed. Bryant and Holli were cooperative in giving interviews at their home in Alabama. After that interview, Bryant traveled back to Kentucky, voluntarily, to take a polygraph. He officially failed the polygraph, as detailed in this case, although he showed no deception with regard to seeing Martin fall, pushing Martin, or withholding any important information regarding Martin's injury."

"Ultimately," West continued, "Blake, John, Bryant, and Holli adamantly denied there was ever any argument or altercation between anyone and Martin throughout the entire course of the evening and early morning hours. Bryant was also unwavering in his assertion that he did not chase Martin."

West goes on to say that, "There is no physical or circumstantial evidence that links anyone to the location where Martin was discovered. In fact, the only evidence we have, such as his clothing, his medical records, the reported physical condition when discovered, and other circumstances we can prove, indicate Martin fell from the concrete retaining wall directly above the location in which he was found. Examination of his clothing, especially his dress shirt, revealed no signs of tearing or pulling at the seams or any other damage which would be some indication he was forced back into that area or otherwise involved in some sort of altercation."

"His shoes only show one gray, linear scuffmark on the inside of the right shoe, which is remarkably similar in height as the outside lip of the concrete retaining wall near the air conditioning unit, directly above where he was discovered. There are no other scuffs around the toes or heels of the shoes to indicate anyone dragged him back there."

In reviewing photographs taken by the rangers, West came across the picture of the chewing gum. "Deputy Runyon told me that he advised Ranger Hogue at least two different times to ensure he collected the gum as evidence. In later checking with Hogue, I found that he did not collect the gum. He cited the reason as being a 'miscommunication' with Deputy Runyon."

"The fact that Runyon pointed out the gum with an ink pen and photographed it," West said, "was support for his assertion that he recognized the significance of this item as potential evidence, which very well could have connected someone to the scene. It may have yielded probative value, but it was not collected."

"When looking at the area in which he was found," West explained, "the first question most have asked is, why was Martin back in that area.

The fact that he was located at the bottom of the loading dock, with no indication whatsoever he was forced back there, is evidence enough that he had, in fact, for whatever reason, ventured back there. Beyond that, there is no objective answer at this point in the investigation."

Several scenarios were conjectured. "One theory," West explained, "is that he was fleeing from someone and ran back into this area to hide, only to fall, critically injuring himself. Another scenario suggests he may have been lured or forced back there where he was either pushed or accidentally fell. He may have gone back there looking for an alternative way into the rear of the Lodge. At the end of the day, there does not appear to be any evidence to support or advance any of these scenarios or any other."

West also mentions in his summary that there was no toxicology report. "Deputy Runyon reported that he did ask rangers about ensuring the hospital pull blood. This was apparently not followed through. With the information that the hospital initially had, it was apparently not deemed as being medically necessary or required protocol to perform an exam."

"On the other hand," West states, "witness statements are consistent with regard to the fact that Martin was consuming alcohol and the substance found on his person was methamphetamine. Thus, it stands to reason he was, in fact, to one degree or another, under the influence of drugs.

"As indicated throughout this case, it's apparent that the area in which Martin was discovered is a hazardous area, and based upon time frames given with regard to when he left the cabin, he likely ventured back in the area during hours of darkness. Ultimately, all of the physical and circumstantial evidence obtained in this case points toward Martin being the victim of a tragic, accidental fall."

On September 23rd, 2004, Sergeant West presented his case to the Barren County Grand Jury for their review of the investigation. Weeks prior, he and Commonwealth Attorney, Karen Davis, agreed to present the case to the Grand Jury simply for citizen review and scrutiny. They did not return any indictments, as there were no suspects developed in the case. Karen Davis advised that the Grand Jury had no further recommendations for investigative follow up. She also advised that no Grand Jury document would be tendered due to no indictments.

After testifying, West and Davis met with Scotty's mother, father, and sister. They explained what had occurred in presenting the case to the Grand Jury and asked if they had any questions. No significant information was gleaned from the meeting, however, it was apparent that both Scotty's father and sister still felt there was foul play involved in the death of their son and brother. For them, justice had not been served.

Seven

On the night of October 19, 1998, I found myself in Madison Square Park in New York City with a white candle in my hands and tears on my face. Standing with a crowd of 3,000, maybe more, I was remembering the life of a young man I didn't even know; a kid who had died a week before some 2,000 miles away, and who had, overnight, become a poster child for gay bashing and hate crimes.

I vaguely remember the police presence, the rioting, and the chaos of the march.

What sticks in my memory is the sense of community that surrounded me and the cause that brought us out that night. My ears still ring with their chanting of, "Stop the hate! Stop the violence!" I didn't join in. I simply observed others marching, carrying signs, consoling one another, and fighting for change the only way they knew how.

I had come to the rally alone. When the protest march began, I was watching it unfold at home on TV. I suggested to my roommate that we should head down and see for ourselves what was happening.

"Have fun without me," Ryan said. He was not about to leave the cramped comfort of our midtown apartment.

"Are you sure?" I asked, knowing what his reaction would be.

He rolled his eyes, as I expected, and asked, "Why do you want to get into that mess? It's gonna be insane. I'm fine right here."

I knew that unless the march was in honor of Ryan, there was no way he would pull himself up from his dusty futon and the Chinese delivery he was currently devouring. I was destined to go it alone. Weeks later, when it was fashionable, I would overhear my roommate speak to others about the daring night he spent marching down Fifth Avenue and his plight to keep Matthew Shepard's memory alive.

At some point in the evening my candle went out, and I decided to sit down near a tree where a group of young marchers had gathered. I wasn't ready to head home and be confronted with Ryan's endless questions regarding the event. For a while I quietly eavesdropped on their conversation. They were discussing Matthew's life, what it must be like for his family to lose a son, and the brutality he endured on the fence. One even commented on how cute Matthew was. The others all agreed.

I continued sitting there, staring out into the dark night for another half hour. When the crowds began to thin out I decided it time to leave. But before I stood up from my concrete seat, I heard one of the young men ask, "Why did you move to New York?" He was wearing a thin, muscle shirt emblazoned with the word "Crunch" on the front. I couldn't help but think how cold he must be in this chilly autumn air.

A guy in a grey knitted hat and black-rimmed glasses that made him look like Buddy Holly answered, "To get the hell outta my shitty town." The group laughed.

"Seriously," he said, "it's full of bigots and assholes."

"David, what about you?" asked the guy in the muscle shirt. "Aren't you from Arkansas?" He pronounced the state with a backwoods flavor and an ending that sounded like "saaawww."

"Pine Bluff. Born and raised," David responded. "My dad kicked me out when I was caught in bed with my best friend. We weren't doing anything, just talking. Fully clothed. But that was enough reason for him to get rid of me. That and the fact I wasn't quarterback of the football team."

"Then how did you end up here?" Buddy Holly asked him.

"A cousin of mine in Little Rock worked in the governor's office," he explained. "She had a best friend living in Brooklyn, doing work for Clinton's campaign, who she hooked me up with. I got on a bus and moved in a couple days later."

"What happened to your best friend?" the fourth and final man asked.

"I haven't talked to him since. I heard he was married though and still living in Pine Bluff," David said. "And you, Mr. Nosey! What brought you here?"

The muscle shirt smiled, "Honey, I am FROM this city!"

Buddy Holly screamed, "Bitch, you're not even from this country!" The group cracked up.

"What I mean is," he explained, "I've always felt like I'm from New York. I don't care where I came from originally, New York is my true home."

I started to recognize the similarities between these four young men and myself. We looked to be the same age; the same age as the kid we were sitting here honoring in one way or another. We were from small, distant places that found a home in the Big Apple. A home with others like ourselves that didn't make us feel different.

I knew I was different when I took my first steps. As I grew older I learned what that difference was and chose to accept it from an early age. I don't recall ever struggling with being gay, at least not internally. But I knew, that in order to play the game in Glasgow, Kentucky, I would have to resist any behavior that might label me a "fag" or evoke a beating or two. As my mother says, I have always marched to the beat of my own drum.

Scotty marched to a different beat as well, but his high school experience was not the same as mine. He was called derogatory names in the halls of school, brought on in part by the same guys that would allegedly bring about his demise a decade later.

I was feeling dissention not by my peers, but the adults around me; the preachers who spoke of damnation to homosexuals, the friends of my parents who gossiped about so-and-so who is "living in sin down in Nashville with his boyfriend," and teachers who made me feel like a second-class citizen. I was more nervous about *them*.

During my senior year of high school, Bill Clinton, another Southerner, was elected president. His military policy of "Don't Ask, Don't Tell" was a hot topic that year, not only throughout the country, but of my Political Science class as well. I distinctly remember the class having a rather lively discussion of this issue when the teacher, Mr. Brown, blatantly expressed his opinion that gays have no right to be in the military.

"They're just a distraction," he said. "Would you really want one showering next to you?"

Today I can easily laugh off the absurdity of his comments, but at seventeen years old, I was shaken by what he said. He didn't want me fighting for his country, and I wouldn't have put it passed him to kick me out of his class had he known. Because he and his wife attended our church and knew my family well, I had to bite my tongue and feign respect.

I never spoke to the four marchers while I sat under the tree in Madison Square Park. They never asked me where I was from or what brought me to New York. No one ever did. Just as I, in my childhood, had unconsciously accepted that I was gay, I think I unconsciously left home for the big city to be a part of those that shared my differences. I always referred to the city as "my bubble." I never wondered if it was keeping *them* out or keeping me safe within.

Years later, when I was informed of Scotty's death, I was quickly transported back to that night. And like Matthew Shepard, Scotty, too, had suffered head injuries, fallen into a coma, and died days later. But there was no march for Scotty. There was no public outcry, no rioting in the streets, no candlelight vigil to speak of. There was only gossip, followed by whispers, that eventually faded into the background. It was then that I understood why I left home in the first place. I could have been the one that night, lying for hours on a concrete slab with blood and the misty rain on my face, waiting for someone to discover me. Would my outcome be the same? Would anyone march for me? Would those responsible have still gotten away with it?

I was having a day in which I was certain Scotty's fall was no accident. The following day I would change my mind and convince myself that no one but he was at fault. And still the day after that, I was certain Scotty didn't fall at all.

For weeks I scrutinized every document I possessed and questioned much of the information provided. With different colored stickers, highlighters, and pens, I scrawled notes on practically every sheet. And although I would read them numerous times, there were days when new details would emerge on a page that I had never noticed before. It was both fascinating and frustrating.

One day, while reviewing his medical records, I noticed nowhere had it been reported that Scotty had a tear in his throat. Jason Blakely, the EMS worker, remembered seeing one when he was prepping Scotty for the flight to Vanderbilt. In fact, except for the tracheostomy, his records showed that his hyoid bone, larynx, and trachea were intact and without obstructions. And what of the abrasions on his left arm and suprapubic area? How did those get there, I wondered.

I was also surprised to learn of the untreated laceration on the back of Scotty's head that Dr. Levy found during the autopsy. Yet, as he points out, there was no mention of this injury in any of the proceeding medical records. Then there were the contusions on Scotty's chest. West was told by the medical examiner that these bruises were not evidence of any type of assault but never provided an explanation as to what might have caused them.

And why was a sexual assault exam not given to Scotty? If there were rumors of an altercation and rumors of sexual advances, why did Karen Davis advise the Trauma Staff that such an exam would not be necessary? I wasn't ready to accept the idea that she was capable of a conspiracy, but within the coming months I would start to believe that assumption more and more.

I thought to myself, how could a six-foot, one hundred eighty pound person fall eleven feet and sustain no broken bones, scratches or neck injuries? That seemed so foreign to me. I would later come to learn that the retaining wall itself is eighty-one feet in length. The chock-block that Scotty's head was resting on is roughly twelve inches wide by forty-eight inches long. In terms of probability, what are the odds, I began thinking, someone would fall from the exact spot above the chock-block, given the fact that you have so much more space from which to do so? It wasn't making sense to me.

Even Angelo Pedicini would make a similar comment during my interview with him. "It seemed odd," he said, "that from where the concrete wheel stop was to where he was supposedly walking along the wall and fell…looking at geometry and physics, it didn't seem to jive in my mind. It would have been a really weird accident."

I decided to focus my attention on the interviews of the persons of interest, as well as Holli Vincent. The gist of everyone's stories was similar. They all agreed that Scotty first approached Blake about oral sex. Then they say he left the cabin, only to return roughly twenty to thirty minutes later and propositioned Bryant. Each one claimed, too, that Blake, John, Bryant, and Scotty were the only ones awake in the cabin at that time. What happened next is still a mystery.

In the report, both John and Bryant told Sergeant West that Scotty basically came out of nowhere, knelt down beside Bryant on the sofa, reached for his penis, and asked if he could give him a blowjob. As is noted later during his polygraph exam, Bryant denies ever having said that. According to Bryant, he told Scotty that he "wasn't into that" and that if he wanted to, his wife was in the next room. John even tells West he heard Bryant exclaim, "What are you doing?", apparently directed at Scotty.

However, Blake paints a different picture. According to him, Bryant would have been up for the blowjob had he and John wanted in on the action. "I'm not going to do this," Blake describes Bryant saying, "unless you all are going to do this." I found this to be very telling.

Then both Blake and John describe John's reaction as "Fuck this, I'm outta here," before he leaves the room. Only John says he took off outside to the top of the hill nearby. Blake and Bryant didn't make that claim, but rather insinuated John headed to another part of the cabin. Yet they all agreed that Scotty got up and took off.

In John's conversation with police, he described Holli Vincent as waking up and forcing Bryant back to bed. Blake also explained that she was in bed at the time of the sexual advance and assumed she woke up because she heard them all talking about it. But Bryant and Holli explained to police that Bryant woke her up to tell her about what had happened. The couple also agree that all four of them continued to discuss the sexual advancement once Holli was in the living room of the cabin, but John and Blake said that they said nothing to Holli. "She's not *our* wife," Blake reminded West.

And what about when Holli went outside on the porch, followed by the other three, to see if Scotty was still there? None of the other guys reported that as part of their story. I was also curious about her statement she made in regards to seeing if Scotty was still there; if he was "alright". Why would she think he wouldn't be all right? Doesn't that imply that at some point he *wasn't* all right?

Finally, the four, including Holli, said that she and Bryant then went to bed with no argument. I was surprised to think that a wife who just discovered that her husband had been in a compromising situation with another man didn't have some type of squabble, whether she caught him in the act or heard about it afterwards. Then I recalled what Andrew McChord told police. He overheard Bryant say something to the effect of, "Hey, he just pulled it out of my shorts and put it in his mouth." Andrew said it sounded defensive. Could Holli have walked in on Bryant and this was his excuse? This may have given a reason for him to chase Scotty.

The next morning, no one can account for Bryant and Blake. According to the reports, Chris York said he woke up between 9:00 a.m. - 10:00 a.m. and was told by the others there, including Bryant and Holli, about Scotty's alleged advances the night before. But Stacy McChord recalled the Vincents being gone by that time of the morning.

Of his own admission, Blake left the park early that morning to sleep at home. This was around 7:00 a.m. Yet, his own mother tells Detective Pickett that he knocked on her kitchen window around 9:00 a.m. or 9:30 a.m. Since the Park is only fifteen minutes from town, what was he doing for two hours?

When I started to review Bryant's polygraph exam and subsequent interview, I noted more perplexing statements, not the least of which involved the mysterious knock at the door. Upon West's inquiry about his wife's departure outside the cabin, Bryant explained that there was a knock on the cabin door that John went to investigate. Finding no one there, he closed it. To me, this seemed like a pretty significant detail that the others had left out of their interviews with police.

Furthermore, Bryant goes on to say that Scotty "probably thought he better get out of here" after making the sexual advance. Why would he say that, I wondered, unless Scotty thought he was in trouble if he stayed?

And although he showed deception for the question of *Did you chase him?* during the polygraph exam, he showed no deceit for the questions of *Did you cause injurie?, Did you see him fall from the dock?,* and *Are you withholding information about that man's fall?* However, one could also conclude that he is being truthful, because there was no fall, nor did he, himself cause any direct injuries. But what if someone else did? And why didn't the other guys take polygraph exams? Were they trying to hide something?

I began to wonder what evidence was presented to the grand jury that would cause them not to further pursue an investigation. I, myself, had easily come across several inconsistencies among the interviews. There was also Bryant's polygraph exam and the admission of Sergeant West that he felt Bryant was not telling the truth. And although Dr. Levy's impression that Scotty suffered from a fall, West even suggests that another possible scenario was that Scotty was simply pushed.

I wasn't believing, and didn't think one could say for certain, that just because Scotty died "as a result of blunt force injuries to the head," the manner of death was "accident." The medical examiner was positive that the injuries came from "a moving head striking a non-moving object." I thought about this. What the doctor was suggesting was that Scotty wasn't hit in the head with a rock or baseball bat, but rather landed on an object, such as a concrete chock-block. But how can one say for certain his head wasn't slammed into that concrete object?

I was giving myself a headache and fully understanding the frustration Brandi had been going through for months. My office looked like a bomb had gone off. There were papers littered everywhere. I had manila folders strewn about with various labels adhered to the tabs. Try as I might, my organization was failing. Every time I needed a document, another idea or theory would cross my mind and I would resolve to pull them before I forgot why I needed them. In doing so, I would forget why I had taken the original document and toss it to the side for later review. I had to be careful, however, that Zoe wouldn't come running into the room, steal one of my precious pages and take off with it as a snack. She loves to chew paper.

While trying to make sense of a series of phone logs, I received a text message on my cell. *Hey Kevin. It's Holli Combs. Let's talk this weekend.*

For weeks now, the two of us had not only played phone tag, but email tag, and text tag as well. It appeared as though she finally had time to speak, but I was going to be out of town during the upcoming weekend. I would have to make it work. I replied.

Going to Seattle. Will call you from there.

Little did I know that it would be over a year later before we would come face to face. I didn't know what she had to share, but I would be grateful when we finally met.

For the next several weeks I redirected my attention from the witness interviews and my theories to focus on the investigation procedure itself. It was no secret how Detective West felt about the initial handling of the case by the rangers. "I'd be remiss in saying we could do just as good of an investigation now as if we'd got it in the beginning," he told a reporter. "That's so far from true."

The Parks Commissioner, George Ward, even went so far as to say that Ranger Adwell "handled the situation appropriately" by ensuring Scotty received proper medical attention, securing the area in which he was found, and requesting assistance from KSP—albeit a day later.

Jim Carroll, a spokesman for the Park, also reported, "The Parks Department has no written policies for investigating suspicious deaths or when to ask local or State Police to help." In regards to the response by Rangers Adwell and Hogue, he said, "The scene was photographed, and there was no physical evidence to retrieve." But there could have been, I thought. What about the gum that Deputy Runyon found? He told Hogue, twice, to collect it and it never was.

I also remembered what Brandi had said about Scotty's glasses. They were found, unbroken, about five feet from where his head was. Runyon had taken photos of the area and used his radio to demonstrate the position of the glasses. But they had disappeared. It was thought they traveled with him to Vanderbilt along with his bag and its contents, but neither his family nor the State Police ever took possession of them. There was no way to check for fingerprints.

I also took notice of the fact that Ranger Hogue had turned over Scotty's cellphone and items within his wallet to his sister. I knew what kind of person Brandi could be when she gets fired up, so it wasn't surprising that he eventually handed these things over to her, but the fact remains, these items should not have been given back so soon. Even Brandi understood that.

Another point I had to consider was the fact that the International Highland Games was preparing to begin that same week. For almost twenty-five years, the Park has hosted this celebration of all things Scottish on the weekend after Memorial Day. Clans from around the world descend upon the area to take part in the festivities. It has become big business, in turn, attracting tourists and their money. To have a possible crime scene on display may not have garnered the type of revenue the Park looks forward to, so there was a lot of talk that the area was cleaned up prematurely.

I had to also think back on something that Detective West said in his summary of the case; something I worried may have been unjustly presented to the grand jury. While discussing Bryant's polygraph exam, he said that Bryant showed no deception with regard to "seeing Martin fall, pushing Martin, or withholding any important information regarding Martin's injury." But that wasn't the question. The question was in regards to Scotty's *fall*. Bryant claimed he wasn't holding anything back regarding his *fall*, not *injury*. Bryant very well may not have had anything to do with his fall, if he fell at all.

And while my mind turned to the day of the grand jury, I had to question why it occurred in the first place with a DNA lab result still pending. West even noted that there was still active evidence. The investigation, itself, continued until the following spring.

I couldn't remember the exact date when the case closed, so I began to flip through the hundreds of pages of police reports I had been marking over and over again. Eventually I came across the final Uniform Offense Report that listed the date as May 25, 2005. There was even a small box above it labeled, "Closed," with an "X" through it. Then I haphazardly flipped the page.

On the next several sheets were lists of recovered property, or evidence, if you will. Scotty's clothing, including his black dress pants, blue shirt, leather shoes, socks, and a belt. Items recovered from his bag, including the fanny pack itself. CDs, lip balm, chewing gum, a name tag, and his reunion book. All of these belongings were listed and detailed, and all of these items had been stamped, "DESTROYED 5/24/05," exactly one day before his case was officially closed.

And if that didn't surprise the hell out of me, what I saw afterwards certainly did. I started to examine these pages one by one. There was a log at the bottom of each one, stating names that had relinquished custody of each item and to whom that item was received. There was even a column for the purpose of the release. Dates, times, and initials were scribbled amongst the pages. Yet, at the very top of the page was a section titled "Conditions of Release." And beside those words it read, "Release to victim's mother (Linda Sanders) upon case closure."

Needless to say, Brandi was furious when I told her. She was upset at the fact that those items were now gone, and irate at the notion that Karen Davis had ordered them so. "Property is destroyed at the request of the prosecutor," she told me.

I was dumbfounded. Was it me, I thought? Was I blowing this out of proportion? Surely I wasn't alone in believing that among the inconsistencies of interviews, the rumors themselves that a sexual altercation occurred, and the sheer carelessness of the investigation, that something didn't add up. How could this case have been presented to a jury who didn't find any sort of reasonable doubt? I just didn't understand. I was exhausted and mentally defeated.

"I find it extremely hard to believe that any of this was presented to the Grand Jury considering that I found reasonable doubt in the first 10 pages."

I had received an email from Brandi in which she was responding to the police report. A week prior, at her request, I had made a copy of the documents and mailed them to her for her own inspection. Apparently we shared the same skepticism.

"There are several different scenarios in my mind of what could have happened," the email continued.

But what she didn't know was that I hadn't mailed her everything.

"There are a few things that I believe and know in my heart, Kevin. One, he did not fall, he was either hit over the head with an object or simply slammed down and knocked out by his head striking that concrete block by one or more of the suspects listed in the report."

I don't know if I was trying to protect her or trying to protect myself. I know I didn't wish to upset her with the items I held back, but on the other hand, she was a grown woman who could take care of herself.

"Two, whoever did it did not mean to kill him."

Yet for some reason, I didn't allow her to have them.

"Three, they spent the early morning hours after it happened creating their story so they could all stick to it."

A stack of papers sat in front of me on my desk. My fingers drummed across the words "Medical Examiner's Photographs." Within the pages were gruesome images of Scotty's lifeless body upon a cold, metal table. I couldn't let her see them.

"And the last thing I know in my heart, number four... I can't relive this."

The other document I kept to myself was also resting in front of me with notes, sticky tabs, and highlighted sections all over it. It was Bryant's polygraph exam.

"Looking through those papers last night brought back anxiety that I haven't felt in years. I cried myself to sleep and prayed very hard. Please don't feel guilty for giving me the papers, I'm more than glad to have them, but I think having them is all I'm going to do with them for now. I can't solve this, I can't change what happened and I can't relive this so I am leaving this up to the Lord."

I realized that holding back the exam was selfish, but I was simply not ready for her to know that Bryant officially failed it.

"I just have to let my weary heart rest for a while. I have too much life around me to be so focused on a life that I can't bring back. My brother would understand."

Eight

On a gray and fuzzy Saturday morning, I landed in the greeting cards aisle at a local K-Mart with my sister. I had apparently come to Lexington to visit my family, and here I was looking for a birthday card for someone I can't remember. In front of me sat hundreds of colorful messages all lined up in neat little rows on the aisle shelves. Behind the wall stood Kim, opening musical cards that played various TV theme songs, none of which sounded familiar.

"Did you find one yet?" she asked, shouting through the wall of cards.

"Nope, not yet," I said, unsure of what I was searching.

"Well keep looking," she hollered. "It's tomorrow."

And so I did. I perused every card within my reach, only to discover that every time I opened one, handfuls of confetti would fall at my feet. None of them played music and all of them proved blank inside. Kim rounded the corner to find me standing in a small mountain of tiny, colored paper, but it didn't seem to faze her.

"Did you find one yet?" she asked again. A very serious expression had formed on her face.

I stared at her. "Whose birthday is it?"

She inhaled deeply and let out a long sigh. "Rebecca's. Have you found one yet?"

"No, I'm still looking," I shot back. I had no idea who this Rebecca person was, but from the look on my sister's face, I was too scared to ask. Instead I turned back to the wall of cards.

From between the metal shelves I noticed two figures walk by. They appeared to be young men, passing to my left. I didn't see their faces. Kim yelled.

"I FOUND ONE!"

I turned around only to find she had disappeared. Yet out of the corner of my eye, I saw a dark figure in the distance, off to my left. It was a short man in street clothes rummaging through a display of sunglasses. He looked familiar.

"Kim!" I called out. No response.

I looked down the aisle but saw no one, then turned and stretched my head towards the other direction. Kim was gone.

"Kim!" I tried again. Still nothing. This time I noticed a taller figure walking towards the young man trying on sunglasses. He was slim and stood at least a foot above the other man. It looked like Blake.

"Kim! Where are you?" I called out. Still nothing. I turned back to the two figures. They had left the display and were walking in my direction. This time I confirmed them to be Blake Oliver and Bryant Vincent.

"Holy shit!" I said aloud. I began quickly running to the far end of the greeting cards aisle. Where the hell was my sister, I thought. I gotta get outta here. I turned the corner and glanced up every aisle. Not only was Kim not there, no one was. Happening to look back from where I had come, I saw Blake and Bryant coming my way. I ran down the shampoo aisle to lose them. But they were there. They had somehow managed to catch up. I slipped on the store's tile floor, but managed to get up and run towards the entrance. They began to chase me. I headed back to the rear of the store where I entered the clothing department. All I could think of to do was to hide inside a display rack of men's shirts.

I waited. Surely they were gone. My breathing was heavy. I felt like I had just run a marathon. I never thought I would run into these guys and now look at me. I couldn't believe this was happening. Suddenly, the rack of shirts parted and Bryant was standing there, arms reaching in to grab me.

Then I woke up.

For a few seconds I stared at the ceiling, counting my breaths. The curtains were pulled tight, but I could tell it was still early outside. It felt dark. I turned my head to my right, toward the nightstand. In dim red numbers, the clock read 4:30 a.m. Then I turned to my left. Kory was still sleeping, his mouth partially open. Between us lay Zoe, sprawled out on our new king size bed that she assumed was meant only for her. Kory and I merely borrowed it from her nightly.

I was now wide awake. For a few weeks now I had been having all sorts of nightmares. Most of them involved the four guys, but some of them included Scotty. Of the ones that did, he didn't look familiar. He was either himself in a different body or he was a bloody corpse lying on an examination table. We were either talking about the latest dance music or I was helping his physician remove organs from his chest cavity. This would continue for another month.

I never woke up Kory to tell him about the dreams. He never knew I hadn't gotten a full night's sleep in weeks. I simply rolled over each time, slid Zoe to my right side, and held him. Tightly. Sometimes I would fall back to sleep, but not this time. Instead I lay there for another two and a half hours theorizing on what happened during the night of the reunion. When the alarm woke him up, I pretended to stir as well. Then I headed to the kitchen for coffee and to make breakfast. Now, for at least an hour, while we readied ourselves for work, I could put my thoughts of Scotty aside.

It had been well over two months since I had last heard from Brandi. She had not contacted me, and as much as I wanted to ask her questions, I had not contacted her. I knew she had a family, a job, and a life to live beyond the constant scrutiny of her brother's death. I didn't have such a luxury; or at least I didn't feel like I did.

Not a day went by when I wouldn't equate a common occurrence with one from the investigation. Strangers on the street began to take the shape of anyone mentioned within the reports. I would search the local Chicago news for similar stories in the hopes that their depictions would spark new theories or shed light on a question to which I could not find an answer. I was soon living the story, breathing the story. My mind never shut off.

I could theorize for days about what occurred in Cabin 507 during the early hours of May 30, 2004, but I knew one thing for certain. Two credible witnesses saw Scotty at approximately 3:30 a.m. that morning. Not only did Angelo Pedicini observe Scotty leaving the cabin after his alleged pass at Blake, but he also stated that he saw Scotty return to the cabin before he, himself, retired for the night.

The second witness was the night clerk, Stephen Foster, who even noted in his logbook that Scotty asked to use the payphone inside the Lodge. According to him, Scotty even admitted that he had called for a cab. At that same time, records with Yellow Cab in Bowling Green show a call came in for a pickup at the Barren River Lodge. It was cancelled at 4:14 a.m. when the dispatcher couldn't verify the incoming phone number, which later turned out to be from Scotty's phone card.

I had to wonder, if something were so bad that Scotty felt the urge to call for a cab to drive thirty miles to pick him up and take him to Bowling Green, why would he go back to the cabin? According to Brandi, he knew she was coming to pick him up at 8:00 a.m., so why leave? But Angelo saw him return. Was he going back to reclaim something? Stephen Foster noted that Scotty had his fanny pack with him when he came to use the phone, the same fanny pack that was found near his head on the loading dock.

The other thing I knew was that no matter what their versions were, all three guys told police that Scotty had propositioned Bryant. Could his wife have caught him in the act with Scotty? It would explain what Andrew McChord said he had heard. Then he chased Scotty outside but sent John and Blake after him. This might answer why he failed that particular question during the polygraph exam.

On the other hand, I thought, let's say one of the guys did chase Scotty up the hill towards the Lodge where he fell, for whatever reason. This person didn't know at the time that Scotty was going to die, so why would he leave him lying on the concrete, assuming that when Scotty eventually came to, he would rat them out to police for having caused his injuries? Even if they attacked him at the bottom of the loading dock, Scotty remained alive and had the potential to get them in trouble. Maybe they didn't chase him. Maybe they didn't cause his injuries either.

I knew it was very dark in that particular area of the Lodge that night. The reports had shown that lights were not even working properly. I also knew that, regardless of the absent toxicology report, Scotty had been drinking, as most everyone else had been, and that Stacey Renfro Phillips saw him doing meth in the bathroom. If he was high, it is possible that he stumbled off the wall by himself. The results also revealed that the scuffmark on the side of his right shoe was the same height as the lip of the retaining wall.

Scotty's shoes also presented no scuffmarks on the heels that could lead one to assume he was dragged into position from another location. Beyond that, there was no physical evidence to prove what really happened. The bigger question I was forming was why he was back in that area in the first place. Maybe he thought there was an entrance door that would lead him to the front of the Lodge where he could wait for the taxi. Maybe he had had to urinate and that was the only place he felt he could go privately outside. I had to face the idea that it very well could have been accidental.

I started to think about the four guys. Were they telling the truth? What if they were not responsible for Scotty's death at all? Maybe they had been wrongly accused and have had to endure the same salacious stories that Scotty's family had dealt with. What if, I thought. What if all this time and energy I had put toward my research into finding someone to blame for Scotty's death was Scotty himself.

Hi Kevin. How are you?

I had received yet another email from Holli.

I don't know if you remember me or not. My name is Holli Combs. I was a close friend of Scotty's.

It had been over a month since I had last received one of her aberrant emails or cryptic texts. For a while I thought I had gotten rid of her. I knew that if a face-to-face were meant to be, it would happen one way or another.

We had discussed talking a while back and couldn't get our schedules together. I would like to attempt that one more time.

I was exhausted from her false aims. I had tried and tried and tried to make something work, but in the end, it always failed.

Also, I have a photograph of you and Scotty together that, if nothing else, I would like to give you. I look forward to speaking with you.

A photograph? Of Scotty and me? I racked my brain trying to determine when and where this picture could have been taken. I couldn't remember ever being in a situation during college when we would have posed together for a photo. I was extremely curious to get my hands on this picture. I took to the computer and pressed "Reply."

Dear Holli,

I stopped. I first stared at the screen, then rested my head in my right hand, my elbow balancing on the desk. My head was pounding with a headache. I took a deep breath and let it out. *Not this time*, I thought. *Not right now.* I cancelled the message.

The following afternoon I began to sift through a stack of medical documents. I was trying to locate remarks made by the medical examiner in regards to the laceration on Scotty's head. My headache from the day before was still lingering.

Clipped together at the bottom of the pile were the thirty-seven photographs taken during his autopsy. At first I quickly flipped the pages to get a peek of the images the papers contained. I had studied them a handful of times before, but I could never get through all of them in one sitting due to their gruesome nature. I placed them on my desk, then turned to the last page.

Not so bad, I thought. In fact, I wasn't even sure of what I was viewing. I could see blood vessels; appeared to be the underside of skin. Next page.

"Whoa!" I shouted.

Dr. Levy had used a scalpel to cut a deep incision from behind Scotty's left ear, over the crown of the head to behind the right ear. The skin was divided into a front and rear flap. The front flap had been pulled forward over his face and was exposing the top of his skull. The rear flap had been pulled backwards over the nape of Scotty's neck.

I was now looking at Scotty's brain. A close-up shot. It appeared wet and was very red, not at all like the gray matter I remembered from biology class.

I thought I would eventually become desensitized after a while, but I didn't. I couldn't. I couldn't handle the images of bone and brain and flesh, especially when they belonged to someone I knew. I gathered all the pages together, tapped them on the table, straightening them, then placed them in a storage box I was using to collect my research. I wasn't sure I would ever be able to fully examine them.

The investigation had seeped its way into my very existence and was haunting me. I couldn't escape it. Days of depression were clouding my thoughts. I felt like I was betraying the case, betraying Scotty, if I remotely thought of anything else. Every free moment I had was devoted to this.

I was driving Kory crazy as well. Dinners were spent in silence as I created scenarios in my head over plates of food I barely touched. Housework and errands took a backseat to research. Conversations never ended without mention of Scotty. And I could feel myself getting weak, feel myself growing tired. The pressure and the stress were taking their toll.

I don't recall exactly when it happened or if there was one definitive moment that caused it. But I remember thinking about something Brandi had said to me when we first met, months prior. *God'll take care of it. Let's just live.* And with that, I did something I told Brandi I would never do. I gave up.

Nine

Sitting next to a crack addict coming down from his high was not how I wanted to spend my Friday night. But here I was, impatiently waiting in the emergency room for someone to tell me what was wrong. I'd been having terrible pains in my lower abdomen for a day and a half now, and I was suspiciously afraid it was appendicitis. Granted, the only reason I suspected this to be the case was because Kory had jokingly made that assumption. I, being a hypochondriac, was certain I was dying.

On the other hand, I knew I was in much better shape than the gentleman slouched over in a hospital wheelchair trying to expel the remnants of his overdose. Two officers stood nearby. They had been the ones to admit him, and I assumed they would arrest him once he was feeling more vivacious.

"Kevin Troxall," a voice announced. I had been sitting uncomfortably for an hour. I stood up and walked towards the nurse. Kory was by my side.

"Have a seat," she said.

I carefully sat down in front of the nurse, she behind a desk. It seemed more like a job interview.

She began, "I just need to ask you a few questions before we can admit you tonight."

"Sure," I said.

"What seems to be the problem?" she asked.

"I have an unusual pain in my lower abdomen." I placed my hands on the area that was troubling me. "I thought it was gas but it hasn't gone away."

"How long have you had that pain?"

"About a day and a half now," I told her.

"Hmmm," she hummed. "You should have come in sooner." I turned to Kory and grimaced. I knew I should have sought medical attention earlier but he was the one who tried convincing me it would go away. Then again, he's a medical mystery. He never gets sick and has a terribly high threshold of pain.

The nurse continued, "Are you allergic to any medications?"

"No," I said.

"Do you do drugs and if so, which ones?"

"Nothing," I assured her.

"Do you drink?"

"Occasionally," I said, again turning in Kory's direction. He smirked.

"How much?" she asked.

I paused to think. Did I want to tell her the truth, or did I intend to tell her what she wanted to hear? I mean, I'm undoubtedly not an alcoholic, but I certainly wasn't ready to be judged by a triage nurse on the amount of cocktails I consume in a week. Or a day.

"I usually have a glass of wine with dinner," I alleged.

She looked up from her computer screen. "Mm hmm," she said.

I was caught. She could sense my bullshit. Maybe I should tell her I eat a lot of dinners.

She pointed to Kory. "Is this your emergency contact?"

"Yes."

"Do you feel like you're going to commit suicide tonight?" she asked.

I shot back, "It depends on how long I have to wait in the emergency room."

She scowled. "Sir, that's a legitimate question I am required to ask. If someone threatens to take his or her life we don't let him or her leave this facility, but rather admit him or her right away."

Great, I thought. Now I have offended the only person with the power to keep me away from the crackhead and in the care of a physician with appropriate painkillers.

The nurse continued to type. "You may go back to your seat," she said. "We'll call you when we're ready."

Slinking out of the room, I headed back towards the chair in which I was sitting previously. I noticed that the crackhead was not around.

"I'm sorry," I said to Kory.

"For what?" he asked.

"For feeling like this and for having to come here."

He laughed and shook his head. "As long as it makes you feel better." I took his hand in mine and we waited. Thirty minutes later I was called back to give blood for testing. I hate needles but hated the pain in my side even more.

Another hour and a half would pass before I was finally led to an examining room. Three doctors, two nurses, and one very handsome surgeon would eventually all come to my bed and poke around. I would be given several tests, including a CAT scan and, ultimately, after six hours, I was finally and officially diagnosed with appendicitis.

"Another twenty-four hours or so and this puppy would have erupted," one of the physicians explained. "It's a good thing you caught it when you did."

"So what do we do?" I asked, knowing that the rest of my weekend was now shot.

"We'll operate in the morning," the doctor said. "But for now we'll give you something for the pain so you can sleep. A nurse will be in shortly to take you to your room."

When the doctor left, I turned to Kory. "Go home," I said.

"What?"

"There's nothing you can do here, you might as well go home and try and get some sleep," I told him. "As soon as I hear when they plan to operate, I'll call you."

He stood. "Are you sure?"

"Yep. Just go." I certainly didn't want him to leave, in fact, I was wishing he could crawl into my miserable bed and hold me until the operation, but there was no chance of that happening.

"I love you," he said, before kissing me goodbye and walking away.

A nurse came in minutes after Kory left. She was there to explain that all the hospital rooms were currently taken, and therefore no empty beds on which I could sleep. I would have to spend the night on the miserable mattress beneath me in the examining area of the emergency room.

"By the way," she began, "the doctor said your surgery will be at noon tomorrow."

"Great. Thanks." I pulled the blanket up near my chin. It was cold in the room. Then I took out my cellphone from beneath the sheets and called Kory.

"Don't bother coming back in the morning," I said. "Wait until closer to noon."

He agreed to sleep in and regain some of the rest he had lost at the hospital. I spent the next several hours tossing and turning while the not-so-tranquil sounds of the emergency room played out around me.

At 8:00 a.m. a new nurse woke me up. "Mr. Troxall, I'm here to take you to the OR," she said.

I was still trying to come to. "What?" I asked. "Now?"

"Yes, are you ready?"

I quickly grabbed my phone and called Kory. No answer. Dammit. I left a message like a marathon orator. "Kory it's me! Call me back now! I'm going into surgery! Hurry! Love you!"

I sent a text. I called again. Another text. Where the hell was he, I thought. A text. I bet he fell asleep and turned his phone off. Dammit. Another call. Nothing.

Still in the most uncomfortable bed, I was wheeled out into the hallway by the new nurse.

"It'll be a few minutes while I get the elevator," she explained.

"No problem," I said, dialing Kory's number again.

"Hello?" he answered.

"It's me!" I yelled. "I'm going into surgery now. Get down here, quick!"

"I was in the shower," he said. "I thought it wasn't until noon?"

"Me too. But it is. I'm going into the prep area before the OR. If I don't see you before, I'll see you in my recovering room. I love you."

"I love you too. I'm on my way."

I hung up and slid the phone under my sheets. The nurse returned and wheeled me into the elevator. On the seventh floor I was taken to a large room and explained by yet another nurse what the procedure would entail. Thirty minutes later, I was still waiting. Kory had shown up by then.

"Hi Mr. Troxall." The nurse that had wheeled me in earlier was back. "Dr. Thomas is still in surgery. His patient had a few complications so he's not going to be able to perform your appendectomy. We're trying to locate another surgeon right now. It shouldn't take long."

Three hours later I was told that Dr. Seymour had been called to take over for Dr. Thomas. However, she too, according to the nurse, had a patient with complications and a third surgeon would need to be found.

"I really don't want to put this off another day," I said exhaustively. I hadn't eaten or had anything to drink since being admitted to the emergency room.

"Oh no," the nurse assured me, "we'll find someone."

To make a long operating story short, ten hours after I had been unexpectedly woken up for surgery, I finally had my appendix removed. From the recovery room where I awoke, groggy and thoroughly parched, I was moved into a proper hospital room. Kory was there to greet me.

I would spend the next twenty-four hours there under observation. My side still hurt, but I knew it was from the surgery itself and not from anything internal. I wasn't allowed to eat or drink for several more hours; simply suck on ice chips. Had it not been for the morphine, I would have hurt someone. Nurses came into the room every hour to take blood, check my heart rate and blood pressure, and change my IV. Their constant interruptions made it difficult to sleep, which is all I wanted to do. But eventually I got to leave.

Before heading home, the doctor instructed me to rest, not to lift heavy objects, and avoid strenuous exercise, including the gym, for at least two weeks. This did not make me happy. I was used to being at the gym practically every day. Now I had to sit around for half the month doing nothing. I figured I could catch up on some reading, which, to my surprise, would be exactly what I did.

On the third day of my forced vacation I received an unexpected email from Brandi. Winter and spring had come and gone since I had last thought about Scotty's case. I had put it aside to regain my sanity, but it always lurked in the very back of my mind, knowing I would eventually have to take hold of it again. It was just a matter of time.

I read the first line of her message then closed my computer. I didn't know what she was going to say and wasn't sure I was ready to read it. I went about the rest of my day skimming magazines, watching TV, and preparing dinner for Kory. I took Zoe for a walk at the park, doing anything to get out of the house for a while.

Before going to bed, I decided not to procrastinate any longer. Throughout the day I couldn't get it out of my head. I felt like the time had finally come for me to begin my so-called quest again, and I had a hunch Brandi wanted me to continue. I opened my email.

I was just wondering how you are doing. I haven't talked to you in forever but have thought of you often. There has been a lot of activity on this end regarding the case. To no avail, of course, but lots of very interesting things have happened. I was able to get the Kentucky Attorney General's Office to take a second look into Scotty's case. I also got Phil Patton to agree to release the Grand Jury tapes to the Special Prosecutor for the Kentucky Attorney General. Unfortunately, after several months of working on it, they could do nothing (that is the short version of the long story).

I have taken lots of deep breaths and prayed a whole lot so I am feeling better about it now. Many things were discovered last year, mostly thanks to you. Kevin, I do not wish to burden you with details that may no longer be of interest but I do hope you continue your book. I'm here to help. If I don't uncover the truth and expose it, I will never be at peace. Scotty would have fought to the very end for me and I intend to do the same for him. Please write back.

I finished reading her letter and placed my computer aside. As I did every night, I put away my clothes, brushed my teeth, curled up with Kory and Zoe in bed and fell asleep within several minutes of hitting the pillow. It was one of the best night's sleeps I ever had.

. . .

The next morning I dug out the boxes of files and writings I had kept regarding Scotty's case. Though I remembered a lot, it was almost as if starting anew. I spent the entire day reading interviews, reports, and emails to catch myself back up. Finally, I replied to Brandi. I knew if I were going to make an impact in my investigation, I would have to hit it head on. I asked her to meet me at the State Park the following Sunday. I had never gotten to see for myself the cabin, the Lodge or the loading dock, so it was imperative that I put them into context. While there, together, I figured we could catch up on the last six months. And so I began my journey once again, returning to my hometown and to the place Scotty was last seen alive and conscious.

Traveling towards the Park I could sense the air getting thicker. It was eighty-one-degrees outside, but felt like a hundred. The sky was slightly cloudy at noon, but I had heard no reports of rain. A new menacing billboard had popped up along the way. "HELL IS REAL" it read.

"No shit," I thought out loud. "Thy name is Glasgow."

I beat Brandi to the Lodge by fifteen minutes, so I decided to take that time and look around for myself. I drove down a paved road toward the rental cabins. Some were marked, others weren't. I wasn't able to find which one was 507. I had always assumed it was the one closest to the Lodge, but I discovered I was wrong.

The road turned clockwise up a small hill to a roundabout of cabins. There were trash dumpsters and a small playground within the area. I watched a young mother playing in the sandbox with her son. They didn't look up, but continued to build small castles.

At the marina I noticed a large amount of people taking advantage of the water. The parking lot was full and the lake was crowded with boats and swimmers. Little girls in two-piece bathing suits ran behind their parents carrying inflatable toys. A lady in a straw sun hat was coating her daughter in lotion while trying to talk on her cellphone. The young girl was fidgety and tried to escape, while the phone kept slipping from the mother's hand.

I drove back towards the Lodge and parked out front. A few small raindrops hit the windshield while I waited. I looked up to the sky. One large, smoky-looking cloud hovered above me. Facing away from the Lodge, I kept an eye on it through the rear view mirror. I felt like I was being watched. An employee came outside and lit a cigarette. She paced back and forth.

Diverting my eyes I noticed Brandi's van heading in my direction. She pulled into the lot and parked to my left. At first I grabbed my notebook and pen, then decided against them. Today, I simply wanted to listen and observe. Brandi and I stepped out of our cars at the same time.

"Hey stranger," she smiled. We hugged one another. "How are ya?"

"I'm good. A little lighter," I said, motioning to my side.

She laughed. "Yeah, sorry to hear about that. I'm sure that was fun."

"Lots," I said sarcastically. "How've you been?" I was studying Brandi's face, hoping to get a sense of what she had been going through the past eight months.

"The same," she answered. For better or worse, it felt like nothing had changed.

"So I'd like to walk down to the loading dock and to the cabins," I told her, "but let's go over here and talk for a bit." I motioned my hand in the direction of the Lodge. There was a small balcony on the south side of the building overlooking the swimming pool. We sat at a round, metal table. Kids were screaming below in the water.

"I don't know how much of that I'm gonna be able to take," Brandi warned. "I hear enough of that at home." We both smiled.

She pulled out a large accordion folder filled with random documents.

"Here," she said, handing me a photocopied page. "Did I tell you I tried to get the Kentucky Attorney General to look into Scotty's case?"

I took the letter. "You mentioned that in your email."

According to the document, the Office of Special Prosecutions had reviewed the case. "Unfortunately," it stated, "there is nothing further within the purview of our criminal jurisdiction which allows further action in this matter. Our office has concluded that an offense subject to prosecution is not presented by this evidence, even if we were to seek jurisdiction over the matter." It ended, "On behalf of the Office of the Attorney General, we offer sincere condolences for your family's great loss."

"What about the grand jury minutes?" I asked.

Brandi shook her head. "Couldn't get 'em. We tried." She handed me another photocopy, an article from the *Glasgow Daily Times* in 2004 with the headline "State Park Manager Retires."

Bobby Lee Hurt, park manager at Barren River State Park for 18 years, abruptly retired Thursday, effective Aug. 1, even though he had earlier announced he planned to retire in October.

Hurt became the third state resort park manager to leave since Ernie Fletcher became Kentucky's first Republican governor in 32 years. Earlier this year, Kenny Vaughn retired as manager of Dale Hollow and Brian Roy was dismissed as manager of Kentucky Dam Village.

The state parks department has been embroiled in controversies over dress codes and personnel matters and recently instructed parks employees not to speak to reporters, referring questions instead to Jim Carroll, information officer for the Department of Parks.

Carroll was asked if the retirement was voluntary or if Hurt explained why he had decided to retire only a couple of months earlier than he had previously publicly announced.

"The letter does not explain why he decided to retire now as opposed to October," Carroll said. "It's just a very brief letter explaining he is retiring Aug. 1."

Hurt's three-sentence letter, provided by Carroll, reads: "For over 20 years I have had the privilege of being a park manager of the Kentucky Parks system. The time has come when I must retire from active service effective at the close of business August 1, 2004. May I express my heartiest wishes for the continued success of the Kentucky Parks System."

The timing of Hurt's retirement surprised many local persons.

Lastly, Brandi handed over a photograph. I stared at it. "Is this my copy?" I asked.

"Yep," she answered quickly.

It was the photo Michelle Huffman had taken of a group of guys attending the reunion. Immediately I noticed the "angel" outline she had described. To me it looked more like Maria, the robot from the 1927 silent film, "Metropolis." I didn't think Brandi would get the reference, so I said nothing. What was somewhat interesting was the fact that this outline completely encircled Blake only. Standing on the opposite end was Scotty, wearing the blue button down shirt and black pants mentioned in the evidence report. Across his left shoulder was a strap attached to a black bag. It didn't occur to me that the bag in the photo appeared larger than the one he was found with on the loading dock. It would be another week before I noticed that.

"Did you ever get a chance to speak to West or Karen Davis?" Brandi asked me.

I shook my head. "Not yet, but I will."

"I'll be surprised if Karen talks to you," she replied. "I got an email from Bryant." She mentioned that so slightly that I wasn't sure I heard her correctly.

"From Bryant?!" I questioned.

"Yeah," she said, "I emailed him a while back and told him that if he had anything to do with Scotty's injuries he should come clean. Then I told him that I had forgiven him."

I was taken aback that the two had had communication. "What did he say?" I asked.

She placed a sheet of paper in front of me on the table.

We are all saddened by the loss of Scotty. I liked Scotty and Brandy both. Scotty was a great guy. Trust me, you have this all wrong. I had nothing to do with his passing away. I am bothered that you still think this. Did you ever wonder why I went to all the trouble to drive to Bowling Green, Ky to take a lie detector test at the State Police department voluntarily to prove that I had nothing to do with it!!! Why would I do all that, because it is the truth. I feel for you and his family. I would never wish anything bad on anyone, period. I am a compassionate person and hope his family can heal from this huge loss.

Sincerely

Bryant

I looked up at Brandi. "What do you think about this?" I asked.

She shrugged her shoulders, "I don't think he wrote it."

"Really? Why not?" I wanted to know.

"Well, he says, 'I liked Scotty and Brandi both.' If he was writing me back, why didn't he say 'you?' Then he says 'Bowling Green, Kentucky, as if I didn't know where Bowling Green was. It just sounds sketchy. I think Holli wrote it."

"His wife?" I asked.

"Mmm hmmm. It just doesn't sound like Bryant," she said. "Just a hunch."

I held up the copy of the email. "Can I keep this?" I asked.

"Sure," she said.

At that moment I noticed that the sky was getting cloudier.

"Maybe we should head down to the loading dock before it starts raining," I suggested.

"Good idea. Then we should walk to the cabin. I've never been down there before," she explained.

We left the balcony and headed counter-clockwise around the Lodge, down a small slope. And there before us was the infamous loading dock. On the right side of the retaining wall I noticed a make-shift fence.

"That wasn't there at the time," Brandi told me. "They built that later."

I watched as she made her way up to the top of the wall where Scotty supposedly fell. Between the corner of the Lodge and the retaining wall itself sat a grease trap, like a large metal dumpster. It was located at the rear of the kitchen just off a riser to make it accessible for the staff to discard oils. I noticed it blocking the path to the air conditioning units sitting in the corner. Brandi had a difficult time slipping past it, but eventually she made it.

It was the middle of the afternoon, but it could have been the middle of the night as far as I was concerned. I felt uneasy standing there. It was somewhat creepy viewing the two chock blocks for myself. I watched as Brandi returned down the slope and walked towards them.

"What are you thinking about?" I asked, immediately realizing that was a terrible question.

She pointed to the air conditioning unit above the right chock-block. "I just don't know why he would have been back here," she said. At that moment, an employee stepped outside from the kitchen's back door. He peered over the edge as Brandi and I both looked up at him. I had a sudden anxious feeling, like I wasn't supposed to be there. Brandi didn't care. She merely sat down on the concrete wheel stop, the one where Scotty's head lay for so long. The employee disappeared.

I walked over by the wall and looked straight up. I was amazed at how tall eleven feet really is. That's quite a fall, I thought to myself.

"What did Steve Runyon say about the footprints?" she asked me.

"According to him," I said, "he took a photo of the area around the air conditioning units where he said he saw a footprint."

"Was it ever tested to see if it matched Scotty's shoes?" Brandi asked, knowing what my answer would be.

"What do you think?" I replied.

At the bottom of the dock I looked up towards the top of the ramp. There was nothing, just a horizon line. I then understood how easy it would be to overlook Scotty's body lying on the ground from that level.

Brandi and I didn't say much while we were there. We didn't need to. At one point I turned around and saw her sitting on the block, caressing the corner of it with one hand, as if giving comfort to the inanimate object. I stood there quietly and let her have some time.

It was obvious that though she had been to the Park many times since his death, it had never gotten any easier. I watched as a million thoughts flooded her mind. She seemed helpless, resting on the concrete seat and wondering to herself, *Why?*

It began to sprinkle.

"Let's walk down to the cabin," she said, standing abruptly.

I let her lead me down the hill. When we reached the first cabin she, too, noticed that it was not 507.

"I thought it was the closest one," she said.

"Me too, but I think they're numbered in order," I replied. "It should be this way." We kept walking until we saw it. It appeared empty. The surrounding cabins were busy with adults grilling on the porch or kids running around the yard in the rain. We both stepped on to the walkway and headed to the door. There was an awning above the porch that kept us from getting wet. Brandi pressed her face to one of the windows in an attempt to peer in. Inside, the blinds were slightly open but very little could be viewed.

"I wanna go in," she said.

I looked at her. "Do you?"

She shook her head. "I don't know. I'd like to see the last things he saw, but I don't know." She tried to open the door, but it was locked.

"Do you think they'd let you take a look?" I asked.

"I could tell them I'm having a get-together next month," Brandi said, "and wanted to see one of the cabins. It looks like all the others are occupied so maybe they'd have to show me this one."

We stood on the porch for another ten minutes, devising scenarios we thought would allow us entrance.

"I could say I was here the other night and left something behind," I told her.

She laughed. "Or I could just tell them the truth."

I joked, "That's not as much fun."

We stepped out from under the awning, as the rain was beginning to lighten. I decided to circle the cabin and see what was around back. Brandi followed.

"In the report," I began, "it said the guys hung out on the porch. I wanted to see if there was one on the backside." There wasn't.

"Let's go," Brandi said. "I'm gonna go ask 'em."

We began walking back up the hill towards the front of the Lodge. I didn't let Brandi know it, but I was timing how long it took us to make the route. I wanted to verify it against what was reported. Just a little over six and a half minutes.

Before Brandi entered the front door, I stopped her.

"You go in first," I said. "Then if something goes wrong and they don't let you in, I'll go and pretend to be someone else with a different story." I could tell she thought I was crazy.

I watched her as she walked inside and headed to the front desk. Then I backed around the corner and waited. Several cars dropped off passengers, more employees came outside for smoke breaks, and two rangers stood nearby, talking. I tried unsuccessfully to view their nametags. I was curious to know if either one was Adwell or Hogue.

The employees soon returned inside, and the rangers eventually jumped in a van and took off. Brandi had been inside for a while. I was beginning to get nervous. Then I saw her round the corner.

"Well?" I asked.

"They won't let me in," she said.

I was disappointed. "What did you say?"

"Well at first I lied and told the girl I wanted to rent it, but wanted to see it first. She said it had just been vacated, but she would show me a similar one. Then I told her the truth. I said that my brother had died there and it would mean a lot if I could see the last place that I knew he was alive."

I asked, "What did she say to that?"

"She said she was real sorry but Kentucky law states that they couldn't allow guests in to cabins until they had been cleaned. It's a health and safety issue," Brandi explained. "Then I asked if I could come right back after they cleaned it."

"And?" I asked.

"And she said someone else had rented it for the night, but she would call me between its cleanin' and the guests arrivin'. But I don't think she's gonna do that."

"Sorry," I said.

"It's funny. Some other guy was standing behind her the whole time and I could tell he was bein' nosey. He looked busy, but kept leanin' his head in tryin' to hear what we were sayin'."

Brandi held up her cellphone and looked at the front. I think she was hoping it would ring.

"Then I asked the girl if she was working here when all this happened," Brandi continued. "She told me that she didn't start working here until 2006 but she had heard about the reunion and about Scotty."

"That's strange," I told her.

Brandi shook her head, "I'm not surprised."

"So what do you want to do now?" I asked.

The two of us stood near the entrance for another twenty minutes or so. Brandi continued to stare at her phone.

"She's not calling me," she said flatly.

And with that we decided to leave.

. . .

The following week I traveled to Frankfort. I decided to pay a visit to the Kentucky State Police headquarters for two reasons. I wanted to inquire about receiving copies of the actual recorded interviews of the four guys. I figured they were open record and wasn't sure why I hadn't gotten them originally. After reading their summaries throughout the report, I felt I needed to compare the actual interviews against them. Important points may have been overlooked during the note taking, or, I thought suspiciously, certain questions and answers may have been deliberately not recorded within those summaries. My second reason was to pick out photos that had been taken during the initial investigation. I was hoping to view for myself what only a select few had seen before.

About sixty miles outside the capital, I called the office of Detective West, now a Lieutenant and the Investigations Commander. When the receptionist put me through to his desk my heart began to beat faster. I had no idea what he was going to say. I had no idea what *I* was going to say. What made it worse was that I was on hold for a solid five minutes. I shouldn't have been driving.

"This is Lieutenant West," a voice finally broke, "May I help you?"

By now, I should have realized that my assumptions about most people are generally off base. Here I was for nearly three years assuming that Shannon West would sound like Sergeant Foley from *An Officer and a Gentleman*. I had already prepared myself to be yelled at by a Louis Gossett Jr. facsimile. But I was wrong.

I explained to him who I was and what I was doing and how I hoped he would be able to assist me with my project.

"Certainly," he said. "I remember the case well." His voice was delicate and deliberate. He spoke frankly and seemed genuine.

"What day did you want to meet with me?" he asked.

I said, "Whatever day works within your schedule."

"How about next Friday?"

"That works," I said. I couldn't believe I was finally going to be meeting with him. I was also happy to conclude that he needn't intimidate me and that he didn't seem reluctant to talk.

"You've had my case, and you've read it," he said. "I'll be quite honest with you and pointed when I say it seems like from the outset a lot of people wanted to make this into something before they had any facts. That was very frustrating to me."

I responded, "I understand."

He continued, "And it seemed like it almost upset a lot of people when it didn't turn out to be what they thought it was supposed to be. And it was terribly frustrating because I had worked so hard."

"Right," I agreed, not knowing what to say.

"Then I reached out to the press in trust, and man, did I get slapped hard for that!" he told me. "I said some off-the-record things just to keep things under control and tell the guy what was happening and what was not, and I got screwed bad. I even had other members of the press, people I had had relationships with for years, call to apologize on his behalf."

At this point I wasn't sure why he was telling me this. All I could conclude was that he was hoping I wouldn't treat him the same way as the reporter. I assured him that I simply wanted to hear his side of things.

"It had great potential to be everything that everybody thought it was," he said, "but the facts were we just didn't...it's like I tell people all the time, I don't have the luxury of supposition and conjecture. That's what readers and newspapers and books have, but I don't have that. I have to put the facts together and I hope the readers can come to the same conclusions that I did."

"Right," I agreed again.

"There's a lot of questions, and the details in there are pretty juicy at best. And people will read it and say, 'Oh my gosh!' But does it add up to murder?" he asked.

I was waiting for him to answer, but he said nothing more.

"Ok, well, if you don't have any questions for me then, I guess I'll see you next Friday," I told him, wanting to get off the phone.

"Alright," he said. "I will see you then."

And that was it, as simple as that. I continued on to Frankfort.

When I arrived inside the building, I was stopped by a glass wall. There was a woman behind it filing papers.

"Can I help you sir?" she asked me.

"Yes, I'm here to see the Custodian of Records," I explained. "I have an open records request for her."

She stood up. "I'm sorry, the Custodian is out of town today and her assistant has gone home early."

Dammit, I thought. I drove all this way.

"I'll be happy to give her the request if you'd like," the receptionist told me.

I slid the form between two panes of glass. The woman on the other side retrieved it.

"Sure, I was just hoping she could tell me whether or not recordings are part of the open records I'd be allowed to have," I tried to explain.

"I believe they are, yes," she confirmed.

I left the building, got inside my car and drove to the photo lab. It seemed much farther out of the way than I expected. Within its own small compound sat the Central Laboratory Branch. The parking lot was practically empty and the building seemed extremely quiet.

Once inside, I walked to yet another receptionist seated behind glass.

"May I help you?" she also asked.

I withdrew a document from my bag and presented her with it.

"Yes, I wanted to pick up some photos from the lab," I said. The case number I'm interested in is listed on that letter."

The woman scanned the letter then handed it back.

"Please sign in," she said, pointing to a registry in front of me.

After signing my name, she waved me through a set of double doors. She met me inside and placed a visitor's nametag on my chest.

"Straight to the back on the right," she instructed.

I headed in the direction given while a security officer watched my every move. I felt like I had walked into the CIA. Through another set of doors at the end of the hall was the photo lab, and yet again, another receptionist.

"May I help you?" she asked. Everyone was so friendly, I thought.

"I'm here to pick out some photos. This is the case number," I said, handing her the same letter.

"One minute please," she said, "Have a seat."

By the front corner were a few chairs. I placed my messenger bag in one and sat in another. The receptionist picked up her phone and called for assistance. A few minutes later a young woman in a white lab coat entered the area.

"Hi there," she spoke to me. "May I help you?"

I explained what I was doing, showed her the letter with the case number, and again was instructed to wait. Eventually Charlie Moffett, the photo lab supervisor, came out to meet me.

"Are these what you're looking for?" he asked.

I opened a large envelope that contained several contact sheets. Though the photos were small I could make out images of the loading dock, the Lodge, and aerial shots of the State Park.

"That's exactly what I'm looking for," I told him.

Handing me a grease pen, the supervisor instructed, "Mark which ones you need copies of, and I'll have them made for you."

I could tell he was a no-nonsense guy. He stood beside me the entire time I was there while scrutinizing dozens and dozens of small photos. It was difficult to make out every image on account of their size, but I picked out a good amount I thought would help. I particularly wanted to see photos of the chock-blocks, the placement of Scotty's glasses, the gum Ranger Hogue was supposed to have collected, and what the area of the loading dock looked like the morning after Scotty was found.

"Wait a minute," Charlie stopped me, "I remember this case."

"Oh yeah?" I asked.

"Yeah. Some kid fell off a wall at a State Park, right?" he asked.

I was surprised. "Yeah, that's right. What else do you remember?"

He thought for a second. "That's about it, really. Don't remember too much else."

I was hoping he would have had more insight on the case. In one week I had already heard from two strangers who were familiar with what happened. I thought it was intriguing.

"Did they ever find out what happened to that kid?" he asked.

I shook my head. "No," I said. "Not yet."

Before I walked out the glass doors, Charlie told me to have a good day. I returned the comment. Then, maybe it was my imagination, but I could have sworn I heard him say, "Good luck." When I turned around to face him, he was gone.

After leaving the photo lab I hopped back in the car and headed home. I decided to wait and view the pictures when I had time to actually study them. Had I done so in the car I may have driven off the road after discovering something completely unexpected.

The first couple of images I reviewed were of the loading dock itself. The most obvious detail to note was the yellow caution tape that surrounded the area. At the far end of the dock were the two chock-blocks, but it was difficult to make out the blood stains. What eventually caught my eye was the grease trap, located in the same position as when Brandi and I were there a week ago. Had Scotty actually ended up near the air conditioning units, he would obviously have had to maneuver his way around that large black container; not an easy task.

The photos of the right chock-block were rather gruesome. A large bloodstain pooled on the side and slowly slipped away toward the drain at the bottom of the loading dock. By the time the photograph was taken some of the outlying blood had already begun to coagulate. I could understand how Hogue thought there were pieces of brain or flesh, as the dark congealed matter mixed within the bloodstain.

It, too, was apparent that the "L" shape laceration on the back of Scotty's head would have come from the angle of the concrete slab's corner. There was a heavy stain that showed me exactly where the impact of his head was. I was quick to disprove any theory that he was injured elsewhere and dragged to this spot.

Deputy Runyon's walkie-talkie was visible in the next photograph I viewed. It sat approximately five feet away from the bloodstain, just behind the left chock-block. This was to demonstrate the location of Scotty's unbroken glasses. I began to wonder about the amount of force it would take to hurl those off his face when hitting the concrete. What impressed me more was to see how far away they had landed, knowing they weren't even scratched.

In the last few pictures I had received were the black bag that was found on his body, along with its contents. One photograph showed the bag open with the items still inside, another had those same items laid out on the floor. They included his reunion booklet, three CDs, a small bottle of hairspray, a pen cap, some lip balm, and the packet of peppermint gum.

Upon closer inspection of the bag itself I noticed the strap that, according to the KSP report, had been cut off of him when the medics couldn't find it's clasp. There was an extra waist strap on the backside of the bag, which I figured is why so many people in the report called it a fanny pack. On the front were an extra pocket and a thin, gray trim just below the zipper. I had a suspicion. I grabbed my notebook and flipped throughout the pages in search of the "angel" photo. Grabbing it out of its folder I compared the image of Scotty and his bag to the new picture I had been studying. It appeared that the bag around Scotty's shoulder was larger than the one found beside his head the morning after the reunion. Was it possible there was a second bag? I immediately emailed Brandi.

While waiting for her response, I picked up the last photograph from the group. It was the one taken by Deputy Runyon that West mentioned in the report. It showed a pencil lying on the loading dock pointing to a wad of chewed gum. This was apparently the same piece of gum that Hogue was supposed to have collected but didn't.

Seeing nothing of significance, I was about to shuffle the photo amongst the others when something caught my eye. I stared at the image of the gum, then rifled through the entire police report until I found what I was looking for. West had noted that Scotty had been found with a pack of Orbit brand, peppermint chewing gum, with twelve of fourteen pieces still in it. What was remarkable was that Scotty's gum was white in color, but the chewing gum in Runyon's photograph was definitely pink. This further suggested to me that this evidence could have placed someone else at the scene that night, but now we would never know.

Ten

Two days before I was to interview Lieutenant West, I drove to Lexington to finally speak with Holli Combs. For years we had missed one another for various reasons (mostly hers), nevertheless I was soon about to meet this elusive friend of Scotty's. Passing through Frankfort, I noticed yet another sign.

Ye must be born again, once of flesh and once of spirit. John 3:7

Then, about ten miles from our meeting point, I received a call from West. I assumed he was calling to confirm or reschedule our meeting. Without thinking it through, I haphazardly answered the call.

"Mr. Troxall?" his voice requested.

"This is he," I responded.

West began by telling me he had thought long and hard since our first phone conversation, and he had ultimately decided not to speak with me about Scotty's case. He said he felt like he, as an officer, should not add or take away from the story.

"My role in society is to remain objective," he explained. "Does that make sense?"

I responded, "Yes, it does." All the while he was talking I was kicking myself for not getting him to meet sooner. I felt as though I had given him too much time to really think about what he would be doing. At some point I began to listen to what he was saying and caught him in the middle of a sentence.

"Because some people say, well why didn't you track everybody down?" he continued. "Well because at the time, the information that we had didn't require that. Trust me, I was getting emails and phone calls and we followed up on everything. I had people looking over it and if there was something I missed, they picked up on it."

I jumped in, "What would it take to reopen the case?"

"If there was evidence that had some substantive weight," he began, "or probative weight in terms of circumstantial or physical evidence, we're gonna follow up on it. But because this particular case is public record, it makes it more challenging 'cause somebody can read it and make the case fit their circumstances, so we have to be careful about that. It would be difficult, but not impossible. Nothing's impossible".

When he said that I paused and stopped listening again. It kept replaying in my mind. *Nothing's impossible. Nothing's impossible.*

"But yes, this case is closed," I heard him say, "as in we believe that we came to the correct conclusion based on the evidence we had. If new evidence were to manifest, of course we're gonna follow up, and if it rises to the level of reopening and representing the case, of course we would do that, too."

I asked, "And would you be in charge of that since you were the lead investigator?"

"Well I was the Investigative Sergeant, now I'm the Assistant Post Commander in charge of all investigations, so yeah, it's my case regardless," he said.

"I'm sorry we're not going to be able to meet," I told him.

"Well I can answer any questions you have as long as I don't get into any conjecture on my part. You know, we're all human," he said. I felt like he was worried his words might get twisted and would put him in hot water again. I understood where he was coming from.

"Officially," he told me, "what people want from me are the objective facts so they can make the call."

I explained to him that I was trying to do the same with my own project. "There's so many sides to this story," I said.

"Whew!" he laughed. "And then there's the absolute truth that none of us may ever know. There's no human way, unless someone was to come forward and say this is exactly what happened. And then it would have to fit, and only the investigator and those people...you know, it would just have to fit. You always gotta think about people's motives."

I thanked him for his time and told him I might have other questions for him later that weren't directly focused on Scotty's case. He agreed to answer those and wished me luck on my work. If there was one thing I had learned from this entire project, it was the very fact he said to me before hanging up. "You know," he said, "human beings are complex."

I was completely disappointed. The remainder of my drive I sat in silence. Never would I have the chance to ask him about the four guys' testimonies or inquire about the specific evidence he presented to the grand jury. I never should have answered the phone. I kept thinking I should have let it go to voicemail and shown up to meet him, regardless. I could explain that I never got the message and that we should talk anyway. If he didn't want to answer specific questions, he was free to refuse.

I would remain in a funk for the rest of the day. It was then that I decided I had to contact Blake and the other guys sooner rather than later. I wanted answers. But how was I going to get them to talk?

. . .

I pulled into the parking lot of the Good Foods Market and Café after entering Lexington. I got my bag and notebook together but sat with them both in my lap for a couple of minutes. I was trying to forget about the call with Shannon West and focus. I took a long, deep breath and stepped out of the car. Inside, I grabbed an iced tea and sat in the window waiting for them to arrive. I had never met Holli, nor seen any photos of her, but I immediately recognized her when she appeared. There was a giant smile on her face. She walked quickly over to where I was seated, and before I could barely stand she had grabbed and hugged me.

"I'm so glad to meet you," she said, wiping her long, black hair out of her face.

"It's good to finally meet you too," I replied. "Have a seat."

Without warning, she turned around and walked away. I wasn't sure what had just happened. Then I noticed her waving someone over.

A girl, taller than Holli, dressed completely in black with unnaturally red hair, bounced over to the table.

"Are you Kevin?" she asked.

I extended my hand. "Yes. Hi."

"I'm Amity," she said. "It's so nice to finally meet you. Holli has told me so much about you."

I had never heard about this girl and had no idea what Holli could have possibly told her about me. This was our first meeting.

"Amity lived with Scotty and me," Holli explained. "We were all close."

The three of us sat down, and I pulled out my notebook. Holli dug around in a large, black bag she had brought and withdrew an even larger black binder, decorated with stickers and photos.

She explained, "This is all the stuff I've collected about Scotty over the years." She pulled out pages and pages. "I have newspaper articles, online conversations with people, pictures..." she paused. "Oh, and this!"

She gently peeled out a photograph. The area around the top of the picture had been cut around with scissors. She handed it across the table into my hand.

"You can have it," she said.

It was the photo of Scotty and me that she had mentioned months ago. In it were the two of us posed with two girls, one being Natalie, Susannah's younger sister and former roommate of Scotty when he lived in Bowling Green. We were all dressed up like we were going to a party. Scotty appeared as though he was still getting ready. He was wearing a ball cap and holding a bottle of champagne. Natalie was holding a 40-ounce beer. We were classy and we knew it.

"Are you sure?" I asked Holli. "I can make a copy for myself."

"No," she replied. "Keep it."

I stared at the photo some more. I think Holli and Amity were talking to one another; maybe they were talking to me, but I was fixated on the picture and had tuned them out. I noticed myself, younger-looking and with red-eye. Scotty was all smiles, obviously in a very good mood. Maybe it was the champagne. I couldn't help noticing how happy he was. Then I remembered it was a night we drove to Nashville to go clubbing.

"I'm so glad you're doing this!" Holli screamed, snapping my attention back. "I've wanted to talk to you forever!"

"Tell me how you met him," I asked.

Amity chimed in, "We met him at 141. Holli and I use to date and we always seemed to be there on the same nights he was there. We'd be out on the floor dancing when he would dance or we'd be at the bar when he was ordering a drink. It just seemed like we were supposed to be friends."

"Then eventually we were both looking for roommates, so we decided to live together," Holli said. "It was us and my friend Rob."

"What was he like to live with?" I asked.

Holli laughed. "He was so much fun. Funny. Sassy. Loved his friends. But he could be really quiet too. Very private."

Amity agreed with "Mm hmm."

"There were times," Holli started, "when Scotty could be in the apartment, then I'd turn my head and he'd be gone. I never heard him come and go. He didn't always tell us where he was going. A lot of times we'd have to pry it out of him."

"He was a very private person. I'd agree with that," Amity said.

Holli explained, "I remember one time I was sitting at my computer and he was literally standing behind me. I had my back to him. He asked if I was going out that night. I told him no, that I had work to do. I turned around and he was gone. Never heard the door open and close. He was gone."

"Did he ever talk to you about dates he had?" I asked them both.

Holli shook her head. "No, not unless you asked first."

"He wasn't the kind of person to offer up information unless you asked," Amity told me.

"DAVID!" Suddenly a man came barreling into the restaurant yelling across the room at a friend. I seemed to be the only one distracted. Holli continued.

"Scotty only confided in his closest friends. If something was troubling him, he'd tell us. He wouldn't tell just anyone."

"Brandi told me," I began, "that, at first, Scotty wasn't going to his reunion. But then later changed his mind."

Amity nodded. "Yeah, he was pretty nervous about attending. He asked us both to go with him."

Holli's face grew serious. "I wish we had gone. At first I told him I'd go, then I changed my mind. I've regretted it since that night."

Both girls were silent for a few seconds, then Holli blurted out, "I don't know why he didn't use his cellphone to call a cab!" She was flustered. "He had called them earlier that day to see how much it would cost. Why didn't he use his own phone? Why did he go back to the cabin?" Suddenly we were beyond the pleasantries and smack in the middle of the investigation.

Amity was again in agreement. "If something was so bad that he had to go call a cab to get out of there, then why did he go back?" She was questioning the situation like Brandi.

"It's not like Scotty to do that," said Holli. "He wouldn't have made a pass at anyone. That's not like him. I've never seen him do that in all the years I've known him."

"And how did his glasses end up five feet away from him, lying perfectly with no scratches?" Amity asked.

"Somebody did something to him," Holli interjected. "It was not an accident. I know that."

I sat there for an hour and listened to both his friends tell me their theories, explain their frustrations, and relive happier days with fondest memories. Holli continued to pull out documents and articles from the binder. She pointed out facts that she felt she could discount and commented harshly on the way the investigation had been conducted.

"No one wanted to collect the voicemail I had on my phone from him the morning he was found," she said. "It could have been a full confession but Karen Davis and Detective West didn't want to get a copy of it right away. It took 'em forever."

"What's on the recording?" I asked.

She dug out her phone and began pushing buttons. She had been saving it for years.

"Here," she said, handing me the cellphone.

I pressed the device closely to my right ear. The restaurant was still loud with the sounds of lunchtime patrons. At first all I could hear was the white noise of static. Then faint voices in the far distance, but I couldn't make out any actual words. I could barely hear the voices speaking on walkie-talkies. Again, nothing distinct. A few seconds later a man's voice was calling his name. "Jeremy! Jeremy!" That was it. Nothing more.

"It's weird," Amity said, after I placed the phone on the table.

I have to admit, nothing I heard on the recording was damning evidence. There was no confession, no theory debunked, no real clue as to what happened. In fact, there were barely any words. But for years Holli had felt like it was something. And she used it during the rants she would blog, I suppose, to frighten anyone into thinking that maybe she had some major piece of the puzzle that would point the finger to Scotty's attacker. Or maybe she held on to it because it was the last piece of her friend that she had. Yet, I had to agree that hearing those few seconds of that particular morning, knowing what was happening at the time, knowing that Scotty's unconscious body was lying on the wet concrete, was sobering. And how the phone managed to dial Holli that morning and record what it did was not impossible, but indeed mysterious. *Nothing's impossible.*

I asked the girls if they attended Scotty's funeral.

"Oh yeah, we were there," Holli said. "I had actually gotten an email from somebody about a little party the night before the funeral; the night of the visitation. We didn't go to that. It was mostly his friends from high school. We would have been out of place. We were already out of place at the funeral."

"Who sent the email," I asked.

Holli shook her head. "I don't remember. All I know is that a bunch of friends sat around talking about old times, being in the band, stuff like that."

The friends of Scotty whom I spoke to all had similar feelings about him. "Joyous," described Scheri Smith. "And so much fun. He'd come up to Louisville, meet me, and we'd go to the clubs and dance. He loved to dance. Or I'd drive to Bowling Green and we'd hang out there. I remember we'd get together a lot and he'd fix fried corn, grilled chicken, and bake Hawaiian rolls, and we'd sit around and watch episodes of *Absolutely Fabulous*. I was always Edina, and Scotty was Patsy."

"Scotty was a non-discloser," told Natalie Whiteside. "Even though we were roommates, he was still a very private, yet loyal person. It took him a long time to share himself, but what an honor that he did. Scotty was so clever, talented, graceful and glamorous, even though he was perpetually in a white tee, jeans, and a ball cap and had the body of a 'real man.' Never took himself seriously and had the most gorgeous smile. Oh, and he would participate in an impromptu dance party at a moment's notice."

Scheri explained to me, "He just loved music, all kinds. But he really liked the club hits and what I called the 'gay anthems.' 'Proud,' a song by Heather Small, was his favorite. He would belt it out. I'll send you a copy."

"Scotty was just so outgoing," Anne Gentry-Garratt said. "He could really light up a room. We always had the best time together."

I asked Holli to describe the day of the funeral. "What was it like?"

"Really sad," Amity interrupted. "It was a miserable morning. It rained the whole time."

"Except," Holli said, "when we left the funeral home and headed to the cemetery. The sun came out, and there was a rainbow in the sky. I have a photo of that too."

She reached once again inside the binder and produced another photograph. Behind a tree in the foreground a brightly colored rainbow stretched between two large white clouds.

"I like to think it was Scotty," Amity said. "That he was telling everyone that he was okay. That it was going to be okay." She looked down at the table. At first I thought she might cry, but she simply stared off. Holli was silent too.

"I really appreciate you both meeting me today. I can tell how much you loved him," I said.

"He was such a great person," Holli said. "He didn't deserve this."

I had one other topic I needed to know about before I left but I was already running late. "What can you tell me about the Gay.com profile?" I asked.

Yet again, Holli dug through her pile of documents and handed me a page.

"I knew Scotty had a profile on Gay.com. It wasn't a secret," she said. "He would go online and chat with other guys who lived in the Bowling Green area, even as far south as Nashville. His username was BGCorpBoi. Not sure why. The BG was obviously for Bowling Green." She smiled.

"But someone posed as him after he died?" I asked.

"Yes," Holli answered. "One night our friend Larry was on Gay.com. He lives in Nashville and was friends with Scotty, too. At least he knew that Scotty was BGCorpBoi. And this was about two months after Scotty had died. Larry, whose username is Housemusix, started chatting with this guy whose username was BGCorpBoii, with two i's."

Amity took over. "So when Larry looked up the profile for this guy, it was all Scotty. Same photo, same statistics, everything. Somebody had taken all the same information and was pretending to be Scotty."

I looked at the sheet Holli had handed me.

"That's a copy of the conversation that took place between Larry and this guy. At least the part he was able to save. He was trying to get Larry to meet up with him, which he didn't. The next day when Larry got back online, the profile had disappeared. We haven't seen it since."

I read the instant messages that Larry had saved the night of July 22, 2004.

BGCorpBoii: wanna fuck

Housemusix: Your sad

BGCorpBoii: so cheer me up with a piece of your ass

BGCorpBoii: I can meet you

BGCorpBoii: where?

Housemusix: I guess that would be in hell someday

BGCorpBoii: so where are you now

BGCorpBoii: I can fuck your ass

Housemusix: Your just sad

BGCorpBoii: you have a sexy mouth and titties

BGCorpBoii: it's cold here

BGCorpBoii: help find my killers

Housemusix: I wish you would stop this. It really isn't funny

BGCorpBoii: I will stop if I can lick your ass

Housemusix: You know Bowling Green is a small town, it will get out who you are

BGCorpBoii: then can we fuck?

Housemusix: Well I'm not sure what you are getting from this sick act your doing, but karma will get you someday

BGCorpBoii: lets screw

BGCorpBoii: you have nice titties

BGCorpBoii: let me suck them

BGCorpBoii: you could blow me

I turned the page over on the table. "That's disgusting," I said to the girls.

"I know," Holli said. "I wish we know who did it."

"I mean, it's really disturbing." I was saying it out loud but not to anyone in particular.

I began to wonder what type of sicko would take the time to create a new username using the same profile as Scotty. What were they using it for? Had they spoken to others besides Larry? Did they think they would ever make contact with a friend of Scotty's who knew he was dead?

I learned that neither Holli, nor her friends, had reported this to police. Years had passed and I had no clue as to how to track down this creep.

"I have to go," I told them both. They stood.

"I'm so glad we finally got to talk," Holli said, stepping over her bag to hug me.

Amity walked over. "Thanks again for doing what you're doing." I got a hug from her as well.

"I'll email you those files of the voicemail," Holli told me. "And let me know if there's anything I can do."

"I will," I assured her. "Thank you both."

I grabbed my belongings and walked calmly out of the restaurant and to the car. I put the key in the ignition, started the engine, and then sat there for a moment. I reached inside my bag and withdrew the photo Holli had given me. I thought about the past hour; the talk of the funeral, the cabins, the fall, the voicemail, the online profile. I must have been twenty-two or twenty-three in the picture. My hair was rather big and messy. Natalie was smiling with a tiara on her head. I looked at Scotty and noticed the same features he shared with his sister. Then I felt a tear slowly falling from my cheek, and before I knew it, I was sitting alone in my car, crying.

. . .

A month later I was back in Chicago, planning how best to make contact with Blake, when I heard from Brandi. I had asked her previously about the possibility of a second bag in Scotty's possession the night of the reunion. I had even sent her an image of the bag that was recovered by the Parks department.

"Scotty had two identical shoulder or messenger bags. One is at my house," she said. "The bag in the photo you sent appears smaller, without a flap. It looks more like a fanny pack, which would explain why so many people kept calling it a fanny pack."

Michelle Huffman would tell me later that she didn't remember seeing a second bag. "I never saw another bag besides the 'man purse' that he had strapped around his body. But I think Detective West knew about the different bags. I remember him asking me specifically what it looked like."

"Well, I know it is not the same bag," Brandi tried to explain, "because the one on his shoulder had a leather strap and a flap over it. I have seen it before and Michelle described it to me as a big bag with a flap and leather strap that hung down below his waist, halfway down his hip. In the angel photo the strap doesn't look nylon with adjustable plastic clips. It looks wider, like the one shown in the police photo. The thing that confuses me is where was the fanny pack? Inside the messenger bag? I can't imagine him wearing anything around his waist."

I reminded Brandi of something Anne Gentry told me when I interviewed her. "He had a bag full of his own CDs," she said, "because he said he knew they wouldn't play any good music during the reunion." Only three CD's were photographed with the bag in question.

No one could confirm whether Scotty had brought one or two bags that night. Some of his classmates would call it a messenger bag, others would say it was a fanny pack. Some said it was large, and yet others described it smaller. Some labeled it a bag from the Gap, while still others said it was from Eddie Bauer. I had just been confirmed of selective memory.

Traci Branstetter-Gentry, one of Scotty's classmates who attended the reunion, even reported to police that she remembered he had a camera and was taking photographs. And yet another classmate, Benji Marrs, reported that he remembered Scotty showing personal photos during the reunion. A camera, photographs, multiple CD's. If these items existed, they were never found on Scotty's person and never collected by police. All of this would remain a mystery, including the enigmatic stranger with Scotty's stolen profile on Gay.com.

After speaking with Brandi I turned back to devising my plan. I figured I could craft an email to Blake, explaining what I was doing, and give him the opportunity to tell his side of things and defend himself. I really needed to get him to trust me. But how?

The phone rang. It was Brandi again.

"Hello?" I asked, knowing already who it was.

"You're not gonna believe this!" She sounded as if she were out of breath. "I just got off the phone with my aunt. There's a woman named Tammy Hickman. She's the wife of a guy who goes to the Lodge with my uncle. And she works in the kitchen. She was there that morning when Scotty was found and wants to talk to us."

"What?!" I exclaimed. I was trying to make sense of what she had just said.

Brandi continued, "According to this woman, she was with John Moss. She told me Scotty had a bag under his head but not near the chock-blocks. She also said they tried talking to him, and he was moving his leg as if responding."

"How have we not heard about her before?" I asked.

"She said police never interviewed her, but she was there. I wanna go speak with her." I could tell Brandi was ready to make a move.

"I'll come down, and we'll go together," I told her. I put aside my plans to speak with Blake, packed a bag, and headed back to Glasgow. For the first time, however, I began to grow tired of the six-hour drive. It would not be the only thing of which I found myself growing tired.

Eleven

Hidden behind a Marathon gas station, only a few yards east of the Park entrance, sits Zach's Market. Inside, to the right, is a small grocery selling only the most essential of staples like milk, eggs, and spicy beef jerky. On the left side is an even smaller dining area one could hardly classify as a diner. A greasy spoon, perhaps. A canteen. Regardless, when Brandi and I entered, all eyes turned towards the door. Once again, I felt completely out of my element.

We both scanned the small room in hopes of discovering our interviewee. Each of the limited tables contained two patrons, save for one. A lone woman in her late fifties or early sixties sat at a back table facing the door. She was smoking. I followed Brandi to the woman's table.

"Are you looking for me?" she asked.

"Tammy Hickman?" I extended my hand for her to shake. She put out her cigarette and stood up.

"Let's sit over here," she said. I brought my empty hand back to my side.

We all moved to the larger table next to Tammy's original seat. Brandi sat across from Tammy; I beside her. I explained to her my project and then introduced her to Brandi. The two spoke of family and how they were acquainted. Tammy's brother had been a friend to Brandi's father growing up.

When we began talking of Scotty, Brandi mentioned that she had run into John Moss and asked him to describe what he saw the morning he discovered Scotty.

"He never indicated that anybody was with him," she told Tammy.

"Well that's shocking because that morning I got there around 5:30 a.m. And when I got there I went out and smoked a cigarette on the dock. I went back in and started prepping. Well then about 6:00 a.m. or 6:30 a.m. John said, 'Do you wanna go smoke?' and I said 'Yeah, let's go.' And I went outside and said, 'Oh John, I forgot my lighter,' and he said, 'Well I've got a lighter.' He said, 'It's in the car,' so he walks straight out to his car, gets a lighter, and as he's coming back he sees the guy."

I began making notes while Tammy was describing the events of the morning. She had a smoker's voice. Raspy and low-pitched. She seemed neither intimidated nor apprehensive about speaking to us. In fact, she seemed pleased that someone wanted to hear her story.

"In the meantime," she continued, "we have a guy who works in the kitchen. His name is Daryl. I remember him pouring grease into this big container out back. I kept thinking he fell off. So I went running down there and that's when I found him. John ran back in to call. First, John said a few words to him."

Brandi chimed in, "Yeah, John said he saw him and didn't see the blood at first and thought he was passed out."

"We'd tell him not to try to talk, 'cause he couldn't, but we'd ask him questions like, 'Have you been here all night,' because it rained and stormed all night, and I remember him wiggling his legs a little. He knew what we were saying, but he couldn't respond to us. He'd try to mumble, but he couldn't speak."

Brandi spoke up again. "Were his eyes shut?"

Tammy shook her head. "I think so, but I don't remember."

"And how long were you down there?" I asked her.

"I was down there until the fire department came. All of 'em live down the road from here." Tammy then quickly changed topics. "And then that one girl come up and she made me mad. She was a Bale. She just pops up out of nowhere. Her and her husband show up and she said 'Oh my god, it's my fault,' and then he grabs her mouth and does like this." Tammy imitates David Kuczynski shaking his head.

"It made her look suspicious," Brandi said, knowing that Taylor simply blamed herself for organizing the reunion where this tragedy took place.

For Tammy to know that Taylor said this was proof to me that she was actually there. Only a small group of people knew that comment came from Taylor, as it was included in the KSP report.

"I mean, you know. I didn't say anything else, I was just listening to everybody. And then Donna Pritchett came out there. She had called Bobby before she come out there and seen that girl." Tammy started gossiping about the dining room supervisor and the manager of the Park.

"Brandi mentioned to me that there was a party going on that night," I said to Tammy.

"Yeah, see, Bobby Lee had a party in one of the cottages. He's a partier. He liked to party all the time, and so they went down there and drank, partied, and had their little thing and then they left. Met in the lobby and took off at 3:00 a.m."

"To go where?" I asked.

"The Indy 500," she said, before immediately reverting the conversation again. "I believe they beat him. I do. Because when I found him that morning he was in blood. They said he fell off the wall. He could NOT have fallen off that wall as high as it was and survived. I believe that…"

I pulled out a photo of the loading dock area the morning it was taped off and showed it to Tammy.

"Where was he when you found him?" I asked her.

"He was about right in here," she said, pointing to an area midway between the chock blocks and the top of the hill.

"Wait a minute," I said, shocked. "You're telling me he was not down here near the chock-blocks?"

"Right, he was more up in here and the blood was running down 'cause there's a drain somewhere down here."

Now I was completely thrown for a loop. This was the first time anyone had told a different account of where Scotty had been found.

"I live right down there," Tammy continued, "and I was telling them after I seen him layin' there, that poor guy, he's laid here all night and I said his clothes were wet, and he had a bag behind his head like he was laying on it. I think he put it there or somebody put it there; it was for his head. I do remember the backpack."

Brandi pointed out the grease container.

"Between this and the wall is a tight squeeze. There's no way you just jump off, or walk off. I believe someone beat him and put him there. I will never think any different," Tammy said.

I asked, "Did police ever interview you?"

"Nope. Never."

"No one from the Parks Department?" I asked.

"No," she said.

"The attorneys for the Parks?" I asked.

"No," she said flatly. "I told Holbrook, 'cause I seen him down here at Austin's store one day. I said, 'You're the one that investigated that boy. I was there and I seen every bit of it,' and he just kinda ignored me and went on. Never was nothing said, ya know."

"Did you see Ranger Adwell come around?" I asked her.

"Well I know he come after they had done moved his body. Everything was moved before he come, because I started to work in the dining room and I seen him."

"So since no one talked to you, no one ever said not to talk to anyone?" I asked.

"Nope,"

To clarify, I mentioned, "Because I know for a while the attorneys for the Parks Department were telling staff to keep quiet."

"That's probably why they put John to it and not to me, 'cause I wasn't liked there. Honestly, it's so bad there, and people don't realize this, but I started making notes of what stuff I done during the day and what happened. I mean it was that bad. That's one reason I quit 'cause so much was going on down there and I didn't agree with a lot of it, so I quit."

"How long had you worked there," I asked.

"Seven years. As a waitress."

"Any ideas why Bobby Lee Hurt retired?"

"Because of all the crookedness and stuff that he done. He done a lot of stuff. And he wasn't an honest person. He liked to drink and liked to party and he done a lot of it on state time, ttate money. It finally caught up to him."

"And that night he was partying in the cabins. Who else was there?"

"I know Steve, out of the kitchens. Of course, he catered the food down there, and he partied too. And I know the Bale's daddy was there."

"Taylor Bale? The girl who was down there that you saw?"

"Yes, Taylor's daddy, Dr. Bale. John Day Dickinson. I think Steve Nunn was there. But they were all three sheets to the wind when they got into the lobby and I don't know who drove or what."

"Interesting," I said. John Day Dickinson was a relative of John Dickinson. Steve Nunn was a former Kentucky state representative from Glasgow. His father had been the former governor and namesake of the Lodge. Years later Steve would find his own bit of infamy when he would plead guilty to the murder of his fiancée in Lexington.

"And then I heard that those two guys clocked out and left the cabin at like 2:00 a.m. or 3:00 a.m.," Tammy said. "They left."

Tammy was obviously talking about Blake and Bryant, or at least two of the four persons of interest. I knew this fact to be wrong and simply a rumor. I began to question the things Tammy was telling us.

"Was there gossip or any kind of talk that lingered around the Lodge in the days that followed?" I asked.

"They talked. Donna and Bobby. Bobby's married. Donna's single, but there's like a relationship there some way, somehow. I mean, they can say what they want to but there's a relationship there. Anytime something went wrong she would call Bobby. She's been at parties that Bobby's been at, so it just made me think that Donna was down there too that night…I couldn't swear on it, but I think so."

"Would there have been records showing Bobby rented a cabin?" I asked.

"No," she said. "He would put it under another name. Everything he done, he would scheme over. If he had parties, he wouldn't charge people, you know. I just got to where I didn't like it. I done it for so many years. And Bobby's son worked there, Lucas, and his girlfriend. They're married now, but when they worked there they never done wrong. They'd come in, just hung over, half drunk, go out there and try to wait on people and I would pick up their slack."

"What kind of person is John Moss?" I asked.

"John is a pretty good person. He really is. He's just different 'cause he's not from around here. He is a good guy. He's different."

Brandi said, "He told me last summer if they knew he was talking to me, he'd get in trouble."

"Yeah. That's why they probably didn't want me around; they only wanted one person involved in this. But John knows I was right there 'cause I'm the one who asked him for the light. My husband used to tell me a lot of things that went on that they tried to cover up."

"And what did he do?" I asked.

'He was a park ranger. For thirty-one years. He retired in 2002."

I couldn't get the idea out of my head that Scotty's body was located in a different location than what I was led to believe. I had to bring it up again.

"You said his body was in *this* area?" Again, I pointed to the picture of the loading dock.

"I think it was more in this area. He was more up here. His head was not…they kept telling me they thought he hit his head on that." She pointed to the chock block. "I don't think so, cause he was too far up this way compared to that."

"From where he was to the chock-block did you say there was a blood trail?

"Yeah," she said. "It was coming down."

"From his body down to the drain. It wasn't just down from the chock-block?" Brandi asked.

"No, and his head was in a puddle of blood," she said. "His head was under the backpack and some of the blood was on the backpack. I'm thinking that during the night he tried to get that under his head, 'cause it was hurting, you know. I don't know. But I know there was a big puddle of blood here."

"Because that's very different from what other people will say," I told her.

"I was right there," she convinced me. "And it's just like a lot of people said, he didn't move. He *did* move. I mean, he moved when we asked him questions like he knew what we was talking about. He moved his leg. Cause he couldn't talk."

Brandi looked at the photograph. "What I believe is that he ran down here, and they were chasing him, and when he got here and realized it was a dead end, he came back up, and they shoved him or slammed his head here, and it would have happened down here." She was pointing to an area closer to the chock-blocks.

"Well that could have been possible, but as far as him falling off the wall, if he'd have done that, he would have...that is high."

Brandi looked at the grease container in the photo. "I just didn't remember that being there, which would have made a clear runway through here and made it more possible. But with that there, it doesn't make sense again."

Tammy and I talked about the employees at the Lodge including the administrative side.

"I was the black sheep down there," she told me. "But you learn a lot just by listening."

"Why would they want to keep this hidden?" I asked her.

"They've always been like that. And Donna Pritchett's like that too. If she'd hear something, she'd go run and tell Bobby. I seen this. There was just little secretive things that went on."

I was examining the photo again. "That makes me wonder about the grass that was stepped on near the grease container."

"Oh Daryl did that I'm sure," Tammy said.

"Hmm," I said, "that's interesting." That actually made sense to me.

"Because he had a great big pot. I seen him; it had a big lid on it. It was over here. That morning I was there, he was out there pouring the grease in. Another thing too, I know a lot of people come out and looked over to see the boy, just to watch."

It had never occurred to me that a Lodge employee could have been in that grassy area.

"Do you remember seeing his glasses?" Brandi asked her.

"No," she said. "He was facing the wall on his right side and his legs were out; his legs were long and so they was stretched out, bent a little, but not curled up. I was so scared he was dead, and I touched him 'cause I was so worried about him out in the rain all night. I quit right after that. I just quit."

"They didn't mark off nothing!" Tammy's husband, who was sitting at a nearby table, shouted out.

"Yeah, they didn't crime off anything," she said.

I added, "Yeah, I know it took a while before Adwell got there. And they didn't tape it off until after Scotty had already been flown to Vanderbilt."

"It was a long time 'cause I was still waitressing. I kept going back to make sure they got him. They have a good staff and made sure he was good. They had to put IVs in him and give him so much time to make sure he's ok before they take off with him."

"I worked there 31 years. We were always told if something like that ever happened to call State Police." Tammy's husband had spoken up again.

"They always covered up everything," she added.

"They didn't want to lose business," Brandi mentioned.

"And this was the weekend right before the Highland Games," Tammy said.

I asked Brandi if she had any other questions for Tammy. She shook her head.

"Do you have any questions for us?" I asked.

"Nope."

I thanked Tammy for her time and told her I would be in contact if I thought of anything else.

"Well if you need anything, just holler 'cause I never got to say anything. They never involved me or anything. But you just learn a lot when you're down there."

The three of us stood up. I got the handshake from Tammy I had first expected on our arrival. Brandi and I left her at the dining table and headed outside to our cars. Small drops of rain greeted us.

"So what do you think?" I asked Brandi.

She shook her head. "I don't think she knows as much as she said."

"I agree."

"'Cause she talked about Scotty bein' up closer to the middle of the slope, but there was no blood in the photo you have. It's all down by the chock-blocks. And I keep thinkin' about that "L-shape" cut on his head, and it makes sense that he hit it on those blocks."

I was in agreement. "Yeah, I don't doubt that she was there, but I think she has selective memory about it. It is interesting, though, that she was there and nobody interviewed her. Not police. And to verify that Bobby Lee Hurt threw a party attended by a relative of one of the persons of interest was also pretty fascinating."

"I guess I was just hopin' for somethin' more," Brandi said.

The two of us hugged, then parted ways. Once again I was back on the road to Chicago, feeling disappointed and hopeless.

. . .

The following week, I was working in the yard, pulling weeds, when the mail carrier walked by. She handed me a couple of catalogs and one envelope from Kentucky State Police. I immediately ripped it open.

The Custodian of Records in Frankfort had notified me that their search for the recordings of witness interviews came up short. The letter stated: *The written case file was obtained from our archived records; however, there were no attachments with the case. A thorough search of Post records as well as archived records was conducted for these recordings to no avail. The KSP will make every effort to locate the records in question. I apologize for any inconvenience this may cause you.*

I was somewhat surprised that these recordings were not housed in the same location as the documents I had already received copies of, but what stunned me the most was what I read next.

I was informed by the investigating officer that the Barren County Commonwealth Attorney, Karen Davis, may have been provided the original recordings. You may consider directing a request to that office for copies.

I re-read the sentence twice. Once again, Karen Davis had foiled my investigation. This was getting ridiculous, I thought, and I had decided to call her for an interview. I was fired up and the time had finally come. I grabbed my phone. I was shaking.

"Karen Davis's office," an older female voice said on the other end.

"Yes, is Mrs. Davis available please?" I asked. I couldn't believe I was actually doing it.

"I'm sorry, she's not. May I take a message?" the voice asked.

I thought for a second. "No," I said, "it's too complicated to explain. I will email her instead."

"She'll be in next Monday."

"Thank you." I hung up.

I was relieved. I could stop shaking because I didn't have to talk to her. At least not today. I picked up my laptop and carefully crafted my email to her. I explained who I was and why I wished to speak with her. Of course, I never mentioned that I was from Glasgow or knew Scotty. I kept it short and sweet and patiently waited until the following week when I received her reply.

However, before Karen's response arrived, I contacted someone I thought might be able to help prepare me for my encounter with her. My friend Jennifer had given me the name of a former employee of the courthouse; someone who had a lot to say about Ms. Davis. In confidence, she asked not to be referred to by her real name. I will call her Kate.

"Nobody wants to talk about Karen," she told me. "She is crazy and power hungry. No one is her friend, and the attorneys hate her. Plus, she has major staff turnover."

I found out later a friend from high school had worked for Karen for some time, then quit because she couldn't take it. She had even filed a report against her.

"Politically," Kate continued, "it is just hard to talk about her because she makes vindictive look so easy. She relishes hurting people who she thinks are questioning her or her authority. Plus, certain local police will do things for her that crosses legal lines, so it's hard to not fear that. So be cautious."

"Great," I told Kate, "You've scared me to death."

"Don't be too nervous about her," she said. "Basically she is a shark with teeth that only reach within her very limited power range, which ends at the county line along with other Glasgow potentates."

Now I was beginning to regret making contact.

"If you piss her off, oh well. Just expect a traffic ticket before you leave town from one of her henchmen."

Karen's response to my meeting request was short. And though she agreed to meet with me, one sentence she wrote proved to be remarkably unexpected.

You should know that the death of Scotty Martin is still an active case and, thus, I would not be permitted to discuss any details of it with you.

I had her, I thought. This case was officially closed by KSP on May 25, 2005 and here she was, lying to me about it. I couldn't wait to call her bluff. In three days, I would finally have my chance.

Twelve

My mom joked that she knew I was coming to town because the weatherman had predicted torrential rain. And they were both correct. For well over an hour I had to endure the rapid sloshing of my wipers to and fro, yet still it was almost impossible to see the road ahead of me. My stomach was in knots. I was wishing I would hit a large puddle and hydroplane off the road. I figured that would be less painful than meeting with Karen.

Kate had instilled a fear in me I wasn't sure I could handle. I don't remember a minute during that drive to Glasgow that I didn't imagine a terrible result coming from the interview. I was destined to be chewed up and spit out, I thought.

When I approached my exit off I-65 my heart raced faster. It was really happening, I thought. Quickly I searched my iPod for any and all music that might inspire and toughen my ego. I was looking for anything that might fire me up. That's when I stumbled upon "Proud," the song Scheri Smith had sent to me that I had yet to listen to.

I look into the window of my mind / Reflections of the fears I know I've left behind / I step out of the ordinary / I can feel my soul ascending / I am on my way / Can't stop me now / And you can do the same / What have you done today to make you feel proud?

I must have listened to the song a dozen times before I arrived at Karen's office. In fact, I was still singing it in my head when I entered the building.

As I walked inside, a receptionist behind her desk was standing up.

"Good morning," she greeted. "What can I help you with?"

I looked around the office before speaking. "I have a meeting with Mrs. Davis," I told her.

"Your name?" she asked.

"Kevin Troxall."

The receptionist then made a gesture with her head and lips that indicated to me she knew exactly who I was, as though Karen had prepared her entire staff for the big, bad reporter from Chicago coming to Podunk to expose them all. Or maybe it was simply a twitch.

"One minute, please," she said. "Have a seat."

The receptionist circled her desk, crossed in front of me, and walked towards a door at the end of a short hallway. Without knocking, she entered.

I sat in one of the many office chairs lined up along the wall in front of the desk. I looked around. It was a very uninviting space. Empty beige walls, save for one psudeo-Thomas Kinkade print adorning the entrance. There were a handful of other doors behind the desk that led to other offices. It was, what I thought, a typical government office. The singular décor was the potted philodendron beside me. I touched it to see if it was real. It was. Barely.

"Mr. Troxall," the receptionist announced, entering the waiting room again, "Mrs. Davis will be with you shortly. She's finishing up something right now."

I smiled. "Thank you so much." I figured I could always kill them with kindness.

As I continued to wait I began to imagine the worst-case scenarios. What if we got into a shouting match, I thought? What if she refused to answer and told me to get the hell out? I was ready to cause a scene I figured. If she had me escorted out, I would just start yelling all my questions for the entire office to hear. "WHAT ARE YOU TRYING TO HIDE?! IS IT TRUE YOU CONSPIRED WITH THE FAMILIES OF THOSE ACCUSED?! WHO THE HELL DO YOU THINK YOU ARE?! I was ready to be arrested because I knew it would make for an interesting story in the book. Mom had already said she would come bail me out. However, I'm sorry to report that nothing like that would occur.

The door at the end of the short hallway opened. A woman a few inches shorter than me, sporting blonde, shaggy hair emerged. She was smartly dressed.

"Mr. Troxall," she extended her right hand. "I'm Commonwealth Attorney, Karen Davis."

I stood up and reached out to shake her hand. "It's nice to meet you," I said.

"We'll talk back in my office." She directed me to the room behind the door from which she had appeared. She followed behind me. Once inside, I again sat down in a similar chair in front of her desk. I noticed that she left the door open before taking her own seat.

"So what can I do for you?" she asked. She appeared stoic and reserved, and would remain that way for the first several minutes or so of our meeting. Eventually, after realizing that she, herself, wasn't on trial, she would speak more freely and be less guarded. I would also do the same.

"Well," I began, "I, uh, let me tell you first what I'm doing, then, um…" I was fumbling around, trying to explain myself while gathering my notebook from my bag. I sounded like an idiot and I knew it. *Fucking calm down*, I was telling myself. I was trying to summon "Proud," but I had forgotten the tune.

"For about three years now I have been researching the death and investigation of Scotty Martin," I said. I continued telling her how, what and why without giving away too much how, too much what and too much why. I never explained that I grew up in the area, knew Scotty, or that I had kept in close touch with his sister Brandi, who wasn't her biggest fan.

"So I would really like to just ask you some questions about this case and about your position," I told her.

Without saying a word she simply shook her head, indicating that I begin.

"As the Commonwealth Attorney," I said, "what are some of your duties?"

Karen began. "Some of my responsibilities include giving advice to law enforcement officers. They might call me in the middle of the night and want to do a search warrant; they've gone to a house and smelled marijuana outside, the owner won't let 'em in, do they have probable cause, I would come out, draft a search warrant…"

She continued to describe several functions of her position but I quickly tuned out. I really didn't care that she reviewed cases and kept in close contact with law enforcement, advising them how to proceed. I was here to find out what role she had played in Scotty's case, but I felt like I had to be soft on her at first. I also didn't want to ask the tough questions first only to get booted out before I began. She stopped talking.

"Do you, yourself, present at the grand juries," I quickly recovered.

"Typically it's myself, and even if it's a case that I've assigned to an assistant, I sit in the room while they present the case. I want to be there to support my staff. If there's a question asked they're not comfortable with answering then I chime in to fill in the gaps, unless I'm in trial or something like that."

"How does one become the Commonwealth Attorney," I asked her. *My God*, I thought to myself, *am I reporting for the school newspaper? I had written these questions down earlier, but they hadn't sounded so ridiculous then.*

"Sure," she said. "You run for the office. It's a six-year term and it's a partisan position. If you're elected, then you're the lucky or unlucky candidate, depending on how you look at it." She laughed.

"So your term would end…" I stopped to let her answer.

"Actually," she began, "I started prosecuting locally in 1999 as an assistant under Phil Patton who was Commonwealth Attorney at the time. He became Judge December 2, 2001, and when he moved up, the governor at the time, Paul Patton, was kind enough to give me the nod for the appointment. So I was appointed Dec. 2nd 2001, then I immediately had to run for office in the spring of 2002 for the unexpired term of Mr. Patton. And then I ran for reelection on a full term in 2006."

"Are you going to run again," I asked. I knew several people who would be interested to know her plans.

"I can say that I currently have a campaign account open and am accepting contributions and have filed notice of intent to run again," she explained to me. "It's really too early to actually file, but you can file notice of intent."

I was beginning to feel more at ease and I thought Karen, too, was feeling more comfortable with the lame questions I had been asking. "What are some of the toughest parts of your job?"

"I think one of the toughest parts of my position is dealing with the victims who can't speak for themselves." Karen leaned in and placed her elbows on her desk. "Whether that be the very senior folks, the very young children, or obviously those that have not just suffered injuries but have actually suffered the loss of a life. Being a mother of two children, the child cases have always taken their toll. We had one in particular, a Mr. Rodney Emberton who shook his child to death, who was four months old and born within four days of my own son. So even to this day I look at my son and I know he's able to play football. Logan will never do that. He's able to do this, Logan will never be able to do that. That's probably the case that has personally stayed with me the longest and taken the most toll because there were those similarities, but every case takes its own toll. Members of the court system and other elected officials have told me that I take cases to heart too much and get pretty emotionally involved. But honestly I don't know any other way to do it. Because these folks need somebody to care."

Her answer had sounded like that of a beauty pageant contestant. I began to wonder if she was telling me this because it was true or if it was simply an act to gain empathy. I continued on.

"Would you say you're a victim's advocate then?"

"I try to be. I don't know if you're familiar with the most recent case we have. The 21-month old that was run over by a van in a hit and run accident? We were in court on Monday and I spoke with the family for an hour and a half. Spoke with 'em again yesterday. And I try to be…with the stages of grief, depression, anger; they go through a lot emotionally and I certainly don't proclaim to be any kind of counselor or psychiatrist, and I try to refer them to individuals who can do that, but I do try to listen. I do try to remember that even if I'm told of that on Monday, maybe they need to ask me that again Tuesday. Because when you're dealing with those emotions, you may hear something and not remember it. You may hear something and misunderstand it. I may not do a good job of explaining it. So I try to be there for the families to listen, to re-explain. One thing I see we run into is there are limitations. Sometimes folks have the impression, and I understand this if you're not in the system, that, well you're the Commonwealth Attorney so you can make anything happen. You can do anything. You have all this authority and power. And don't get me wrong, I have an awesome responsibility and I don't take that lightly. On the other hand, I can't always do what folks want me to do. Just going back to this case, the family was a little upset and made a remark in the local paper that this person was only looking to receive one to five years and they thought she should get more time. And I told 'em, I agree with you, as a mother; as a prosecutor I agree with you. But the law, you know. We have three branches of government, separation of power, so a lot of times there may be concerns that I can't address, except to say that's the law. Well why does the defendant have more rights than the victims? Well that's the law. Well why do they get to ask for multiple continuances and we have to wait. Well that's the law. So that's frustrating for families and for us."

"I would imagine working in a small town where everybody seems to know everybody, it's probably tough to prosecute or work against families that you know in town. How do you deal with that?"

"If it's immediate family I step aside. If I went to school with this person or I worked at McDonald's with this person when I was 16 or whatever, like you said, it is a small community, generally no, I haven't found that difficult and here's why. If an officer calls me in the middle of the night and say we found this big marijuana grow, I'll ask how many plants or one defendants, two defendants, whatever, blah, blah, blah. And

I'll come in the office the next morning and I'll be like 'did you all hear about the big marijuana bust last night. It was over on Semital Lane or blah, blah, blah,' and they'll ask 'Well who was it?' 'Oh I don't know.'" Karen laughed. "'Well you didn't ask the name?' 'Well no because the name's not important to me.' I mean, what's important to me are the facts. Does it meet the elements of the crime? Can I prove the case? So I don't put a lot of stock, and frankly I don't think I should put a lot of stock in who it is. It's what the behavior was."

"Did you know the Martin family prior to that case?"

Karen shook her head. "No," she said.

"Did you know of the four persons of interest in that case or their families?"

"When you say persons of interest..." Karen paused to allow me explain further.

"Well in the report there are four persons of interest. Blake Oliver, John Dickinson, Bryant Vincent, and Chris York?"

"Do I know those four young men? No, I do not. Did I find out that, later in the investigation, the Oliver boy was Sheila Oliver's son? Yes. Did I find out that the Dickinson boy was related to my first political opponent, Temple Dickinson? Yes. The other two you mentioned...if I was made aware of that, I don't remember at this point."

"Fair enough," I said. Now was the time to begin the serious questioning. I wondered if I would have a cell to myself or if they'd throw me into some group hold-up. "In your email to me you said that this case was still active." I reached into my bag for a document then handed it to her. "But KSP closed this case on May 25, 2005."

"I was never informed that they closed the case," she said. "Regardless of whether the KSP deem it closed or whatever, if something were to come up, I would want to be able to be the prosecutor prosecuting this case. And if I said something that I should not say at this point that would cause me to have to recuse later or would taint this case in any way, I would not want to do that to Mr. Martin or his family. So personally, this office has never closed his case."

I understood her statement, although it sounded like a stock answer. But how could she not know that the State had officially closed this case?

"Having said that, and you don't have to answer directly to the specifics but, when KSP presented Bryant Vincent with a polygraph exam, he officially failed it. Are polygraph exams admissible in a grand jury?"

"Polygraph exam results are not admissible in court. I guess arguably a grand jury could be told of that. Of course if the grand jury were to indict on something that's later not admissible in court, then in my opinion, a prosecutor could be setting herself up for failure. If you do have some legal background you understand the principles of double jeopardy. I feel like I can share with you, without saying anything that would taint the case, that absolutely every piece of evidence presented to me was told to this grand jury and the presentation is the longest grand jury presentation I have ever had in any case, death or otherwise."

"Really?" I asked with surprise.

"I can tell you this because I pulled the docket for that day." Karen opened a manila folder and began reading. "Grand jury presentation was on September 23, 2004. The family was requested to be in the courthouse. Presentation was Sergeant Shannon West. It started at approximately 1:10 p.m. and went until 4:00 p.m. So almost three hours on just the one case."

"Is that uncommon?"

"That's very uncommon. I can tell you that the majority of cases... Now again, it depends on the nature of the case, I don't want to mislead you, but for example, other cases that were set that day which were different types of cases... Possession of marijuana, possession of meth, possession of handgun by convicted felon, DUI, manufacturing meth, took 10-15 minutes per case. This one took three hours."

I couldn't help but notice the enormous stack of pages from which she was reading. "Obviously you're looking at a document there. In the KSP report it says that since there were no indictments, you advised that no grand jury documents would be tendered..."

Suddenly there was a commotion at the receptionist's desk. A middle-aged man had walked inside and was greeting everyone in the front offices.

Apparently they all knew him. "HEEEYYYY!" he shouted.

Karen stood up, walked to her office door, and shut it.

"I'm sorry," she said. "We don't need everyone hearing our conversation. What were you saying again?"

"In the report," I repeated, "West mentions that there were no jury documents tendered. Is that common, uncommon? How do you have proof that there was a grand jury that day?"

"We have the grand jury tape and it's been transcribed. We've got transcripts. When the Martin family complained on me to the attorney general's office, they contacted me. I sent them the transcript and the tape. They have since reviewed it and said everything was in order."

When did the family complain to the attorney general's office, I wondered? This was the first time I had heard that. I was sure Brandi would have mentioned that if it were true. I continued my questioning.

"The report also mentions there was no case number assigned either."

"I don't know how they do it in Chicago or New York. The standard here that we've always followed is that if it is a...let me go back a minute. Cases come to this office three different ways."

For the next ten minutes, Karen explained to me how certain cases would be brought to her and how they could or could not be assigned case numbers. Trust me when I say that her tedious explanation filled with legal jargon and mundane particulars is not worth re-telling. Suffice it to say, in order to keep Scotty's case from becoming public record, a case number was not given at the time of the grand jury.

"There's actually a complicated process that does go on in trying to decide the best way to move a case," Karen mentioned. "In this case I don't think I'd be tainting it to say I spoke with law enforcement on numerous occasions. I spoke with Mr. Martin's sister Brandi. You know, we had several emails phone conversations. And I do remember having a conversation with Shannon West, saying that, based on the evidence we have at this time, do we present it to a grand jury or do we wait, and I said let's talk to the family. The family said go ahead and present it and so I presented all our information to a grand jury."

"Based on the family's request? I asked to confirm.

"Well that was part of the equation," she said.

"How long do you wait, or rather, when do you decide to take a case to the grand jury?"

"Well again, if we're waiting on lab results, I always try to wait on those, because especially in today's society with the *CSI* shows, juries are expecting fingerprints, hair analysis, some extreme things. So if we're waiting on those lab results, that's always one factor. Another factor is the flight issue that I mentioned earlier. So there are different things. Again, I consult with the family. How strong is our case? How likely is it that if we wait a little while our case will get stronger? Does it seem like our leads have dried up? And again each case is kind of it's own animal so to speak."

"Yeah, 'cause I know in this particular one there were reports that there was still active evidence and a lab result pending, but it went ahead anyway. I'm assuming from what you said earlier that even if nothing comes out of that particular grand jury, once the DNA comes back and if something shows up, then you can do it again."

"That is one good thing about grand jury," she said. "The double jeopardy that I spoke about earlier, doesn't apply to grand jury; at least not in the same way. So if we take a case to the grand jury and they don't indict, but say we thought it was a safety issue; say it's one of these child cases where the child has not been removed from the home and she's still in the home with this nasty person, then I may go ahead and present it to the grand jury without the DNA results. Then say four months later I get the DNA evidence, I come back and say it was his semen, I can present it to a new grand jury. Now if it's just the same evidence, again I don't want to mislead you, I don't want to keep presenting that to a different grand jury hoping to get a different result from twelve different people, but if there's additional proof then I would not be precluded from presenting the case again to a subsequent grand jury."

"Is there a finite amount of grand juries that you can have?"

"No, there's no statute of limitations on felony crimes."

I was ready to bring out the big guns. "In this particular case there was evidence that, before it closed, was decidedly destroyed. Was that something that the lead detective does, or is that something the prosecutor decides on?"

"That's the first I've heard of that," Karen replied.

"Really?!" That certainly wasn't the answer I was expecting.

"Anytime I'm requested or I'm asked about destroying evidence, I tell them no. Let me give you an example. In 1983 Herman and Mae Matthews were killed by David Leroy Skaggs. He got the death penalty. Fast forward to 2002, when I first took office. The first thing I had to do was a death penalty trial because he was on his last appeal. Luckily our officers and clerks had done what they were supposed to do. I was able to open boxes of evidence from 1983, some of which were black and white photographs which cracked me up. And I even had the victim's purse that he had taken out of the victim's house that they had maintained, and the weapon, obviously. There was a ballpeen hammer involved and the shoe that she ran out of when she was running through the house. That stuff needs to be maintained. Nate Wood that shot Anna Jones in front of Farmers RECC, drug her down the road out in the county. That happened in 2002. That was our other big trial that year. KSP calls me periodically asking 'can we destroy the evidence in the Nate Wood case 'cause it's taking up a big chunk of our evidence room' and I always write back, no you cannot because he can keep appealing. Maybe I watched too much Perry Mason as a kid, but who's to say somebody doesn't make a deathbed confession or, you know, people seem to get looser lips as time passes and they think they're quote-unquote safe. So I never instructed anybody to destroy any evidence in that case."

"Do you have any idea why they would do that?"

"No, I can't speak for them."

"OK. It was stamped *"Destroyed"* and it has the date, which was the date before KSP officially closed it as well. Would that make it harder…"

Karen interrupted me. "Since I don't know exactly what evidence it is you're speaking of it would be hard for me to say, but if it's something that was tested and we've got the test results and the item itself is not important, then probably not."

"Why do you think this particular case still gets talked about? Or do you think it does? Obviously you've mentioned other cases from the past that are still in your mind."

"I guess I don't necessarily have a sense that this one gets talked about any more or less than any other sensational cases around here except maybe David Leroy Skaggs. Everybody knows it was a homicide, it was not an accident and that's he's the one responsible. Nate Wood. People still talk about that, but they know it was intentional and not an accident, and who's responsible. Um, I may not be the best to ask because I'm in the concrete jungle, as we call it around here, and I don't get out in 'normal life' much. I would probably liken this case more to, because of the un…"

At this point Karen abruptly stopped speaking. It caught me a bit off guard but I could tell she was trying to form her words diplomatically. I figured she wanted to tell me that she knew there were still unanswered questions in Scotty's case.

"I know," she started up again, "that the family feels like there are unanswered questions. But I feel like I can tell you this with some certainty too, even in cases that have pled guilty, have gone to trial, we know for sure what happened and who did it, there are still unanswered questions. I've never been a family member of something that tragic, but I think one reason I went into this business is because I wanted to get to the truth of the matters. I like to know why. I've got that curiosity bug. And not just that, but the truth is important. But you never get all your questions answered."

Not only was Karen speaking for herself, but I would also come to find she was foretelling my own ending.

"So West says he feels like he has to remain objective and he feels like he did the best he could under the circumstances. I know that the Parks Department started to investigate, didn't do the greatest of jobs, and then KSP took over. Do you feel like you did the best job as the prosecutor?"

"Oh absolutely. I mean, is there ever any case where you say maybe I should have said this or done this? Maybe. But I guess to get down to brass tacks as far as any rumors or allegations by family of Mr. Martin or anyone else who said it was a cover-up, Mrs. Davis was involved, I can guarantee you 150,000 % that that's not the case. Because I don't care who any of these boys, girls or anybody else at the reunion at the State Park, if somebody did something wrong to Mr. Martin, then they need to be held accountable. Now whether that couldn't happen six years ago, whether that's six years from now, and that's why I said earlier, if there's ever evidence of foul play, I want to be able to speak for Jeremy Scott Martin. And your questions earlier, not to be crude, but I don't give a rat's ass if it's Shelia Oliver, Dickinson, or anybody else. Frankly, when I get calls in other cases, not this case, let me be clear. But I've gotten calls in other cases that say 'well this boy comes from a good family, you need to probate him. This girl comes from a good family you need to amend the charge.' This has always been my response; I don't care who your family is. And if you think you come from a quote-unquote good family, then you should know better and should be held to a higher standard."

I had definitely come to a place where I didn't fear her anymore. And though I didn't want to admit it to myself, I believed her.

She continued. "I don't harbor any ill feelings for the Martin family. I actually sympathize and empathize to the extent I didn't suffer their loss. But I would imagine that they've been looking for someone to blame since day one, and when the grand jury wasn't able to give that to them, then I was the last person they talked to about this. I understand the transfer of emotion. I hate it because… I mean, I do my job…what's most important to me whether I ever get elected again or not, is that I can look at myself in the mirror every morning. And I know when it comes to this case and every other case that I've dealt with that I can look in the mirror. I can meet with the victims even if they're angry with me. I can look 'em in the eye and say, 'I promise you I did everything in this case that I could.' Well, is this case perfect? No. Now you alluded to some things earlier and I'm not going to badmouth anybody or any agency. We're all human. I'm sure I made mistakes. But did I do everything at the time that I could? Yes. And often there is distrust of the system. And don't get me wrong, some of it is…"

"Justified?" I inserted.

"Yes, even being in the system I understand that, and I don't fault folks for that. On the other hand, sometimes, things just are what they are. I can tell you, and it is born out of the grand jury recording, that I *did* have an indictment ready, and I said 'you tell me what person's name to put at the top of it and we'll fill in the name and we'll indict somebody.' But the grand jury could not conclude that there was any name to put at the top of the indictment."

She shrugged her shoulders.

"And I can honestly say that Shannon and I both agonized over this case. We both cared about this case. I'll be glad to vouch for him, not that he needs that."

Her mention of Detective West reminded me of another topic. "I filed an open records request for the recordings of the witness interviews, and the Custodian in Frankfort said that they didn't have them; that maybe you did."

"That's the first time I've heard that too," she said. Again, not what I was expecting to hear.

"They were surprised to find that they weren't archived with the rest of his file," I told her.

Karen dug through her files again. "Here are the police reports and accompanying documentation that we subpoenaed like the cab records we tracked down and Park records. Here are the Vanderbilt medical records that we have. And we have a couple newspaper clippings."

"But not the actual recordings?" I asked again.

"No," she said. "I don't even mind telling you I told my grand jury person to immediately subpoena his medical records from Vanderbilt, the EMS records, the stat flight records. Holbrook was going to ask Vanderbilt about doing a sexual assault kit on Martin because there were allegations of that. It was recommended they get statements from all the folks that were in the cabin that night. We got the victim's cellphone records, we subpoenaed AT&T, contacted the cook, John Moss, tracked down the pay phone, the 911 call from the Lodge."

"You mentioned the sexual assault exam. Did they perform one?"

"I honestly can't remember at this juncture. I'm thinking that there was something about the injuries to the head and how that might affect his responses neurological. You'd probably have to ask Trooper Holbrook."

"That's ok, I'll tell you." I caught myself smirking while pulling out a document from my bag. "In the report it says that Holbrook contacted you to find out. There was no one on staff at Vandy to do one at the time. And he called you to ask what to do, and in the report he writes that you spoke to the staff and advised that none was necessary. Why would you deem that so?"

"I honestly don't remember," Karen said. She seemed to be thinking about it. "For some reason I had a faint recollection that they didn't want to disturb him because of what was going on neurologically, but I can't say. That's just a faint recollection."

At this point I had pretty much had all my questions answered. I thanked her for her time. "Do you have any questions for me?"

"No, and I'm sorry, I didn't mean to appear defensive or anything."

"I didn't think so at all." I had a sense that she felt passionate about her work and had honestly wanted to set the record straight.

She mentioned, "I guess if there's anything I would want to get out there, which is not why I agreed to meet with you, I just felt like I should, but it's, we take these cases very seriously. I do take these cases very much to heart and I do invest a lot of time and energy and blood, sweat and tears, and I should. Anybody should."

I had to admit that I was pleased with the outcome of our meeting and relieved that I wasn't going to have to spend the rest of the day behind bars. Before I left her office and returned home, Karen wanted me to note one other thing.

"I don't have anything to hide in this case or any other," she said. "What you see is what you get."

Thirteen

Several weeks had passed since my return from meeting with Karen Davis. I awoke one morning and remained lying in bed for a couple of hours before finally moping around the house. My shoulders ached. My neck was tight. I was exhausted for no reason. Drinking a cup of coffee, I casually perused the morning paper. Buried within the news was a blurb about Lawrence King. The father of the accused boy who allegedly killed Lawrence had been found dead in his home. No foul play was suspected. His son's trial wouldn't begin for another two years.

I thought about Lawrence King for the rest of the morning. This was a fairly high profile killing, and yet, I felt, it wasn't getting the coverage I thought it should. Certainly the gay press was reporting quite frequently about it, but the mainstream media seemed to stay clear. Then I thought about Scotty and how discussions suddenly stopped after the grand jury. Aside from a handful of his family and friends, no one seemed to question what had happened. No one seemed to think it odd that, although Scotty had died under mysterious circumstances, the case was closed. Southerners are good at sweeping things under the rug, and in this case, the rug was nailed to the floor.

I realized that this sense of apathy that had simply settled in was what bothered me most about Scotty's case. No one cared. No one refuted the grand jury's decision, though there was plenty of evidence to suggest something fishy. No one reformed policies to alter how state park officials should handle cases like this should they happen in the future. No official was reprimanded or asked to step down for the way the investigation was handled. In fact, the only personnel changes that occurred were Lieutenant West who was promoted and Bobby Hurt who took early retirement. For better or worse, everything simply went back to normal in Glasgow.

I opened my laptop. Two emails remained in my Inbox that I had received and read the day before. One was from Taylor Bale Kuczynski. I had requested an interview, but she refused. The only thing she would say was, "It was a great time, up until the next morning when I was awakened by a terrible phone call. It was a tragic, horrific experience for me. I really would rather not relive it." Then she wished me well.

The other email came from Shannon West. A week earlier he had written to tell me that an assistant had discovered the recordings of the witness interviews and assured me copies. In this new email, however, I was told that the assistant was misinformed and the recordings were from a different investigation. To date, the recordings I sought have never been found.

Both emails were disappointing news, but neither surprised me. Nothing about this investigation surprised me anymore. Well, almost nothing.

Later that afternoon I received a surprising email from Brandi. She had made contact with Blake. During one of our first correspondences she told me that she would send him random emails in the hopes of getting a response. She never got any. She explained that she would craft them in ways with the hope that his reply would reveal a confession or at least offer information of which she was unaware. But this time was different. This time she blatantly asked how he could possibly sleep at night. It must have triggered some emotion because this time Blake did respond.

This news should have gotten me excited, but it didn't. In fact, I was pissed. Reading his response, I sat there fuming. Angry not because of what he said, but that Brandi had made contact with him, that he was opening up to her, and that I had spent weeks devising an intricate plan to get him and the others to speak with me; and yet now, I assumed, it was ruined.

I understood how passionate Brandi was and how strong her desire to know the truth. But the fact of the matter was she had gotten to him first and I knew that her intense passion had the potential to build a thicker wall around him that would be tough to break through. She had always been at the center of this storm. She had always been the outspoken one, posting comments and theories about the case. And yet here she was, getting him to respond defensively.

I understood that I, an outsider, should be the one to deal with Blake. I didn't pose the same kind of threat that Brandi did. I knew I could remain calm and impartial and get him to let down some of those defenses. Now I was forced to revise my plan and I wasn't quite sure how. I read Blake's response.

"*Brandi,*" he began, "*Against the advice of every person I know and share your emails with I am going to respond briefly. God lets me sleep fine at night. I and anyone I know didn't injure Scotty. It makes me sad and I can't believe you would even say that to me!! It makes me sad that you (we) don't have closure and that Scotty is no longer with us.*

I wish that you and your family had closure. I wish all of us that have lived this had closure and knew what happened to Scotty.

I hope that you find all the answers you are looking for but I DON'T know what happened to him!!!

I would be doing all the same things you are, asking the same questions and following up on every detail if something like this happened to my brother and I didn't know what happened. I truly wish that you had the answers you are looking for so that you could put this to rest. I just don't know how to help you.... There is no one in this world that wants you to find the answers you are looking for more than me and the others that have been falsely accused by people constantly spreading false rumors.

I will never understand how all the rumors were started but I sure wish they wouldn't have included the innocent people that have no idea what happened to Scotty.

Brandi... I swear on everything in this world and to God that I don't know what happened to Scotty. The people that are circulating the rumors don't know what happened to him either. If you and others keep pointing the finger at the innocent, you, I or anyone else will never learn the truth."

Brandi told me that he went on to say he wanted to talk to her; that he's wanted to for years, but others in his life had advised against it. From his email, she assumed, he was ready to finally speak. Unfortunately, she would not hear from him again, and not for lack of trying.

I wasn't sure that moment was the right time for me to request a meeting with Blake, or with any of the guys actually, but I was tired of the silence. If these guys had nothing to do with Scotty's injuries, they needed to talk. And I wanted to be the one they told. So I carefully crafted an email to Blake and sent it out. Twice.

In it I explained how long I had been working on my investigation; how I had poured over hundreds of documents and photos and reports; spoken to multiple people involved in the case, and after doing all that, I didn't believe he was guilty of any wrongdoing. It wasn't entirely true. Sure, I had been ready to accuse of him of taking part in Scotty's injuries earlier, but I had also spent days believing that he truly knew nothing about Scotty's fall. I felt like, if I could get Blake to trust me, to believe that I found him innocent, he would be more likely to speak; Bryant as well. I would never hear back from any of them. They would remain silent.

. . .

It was nearing the end of spring when I paid one more visit to the State Park. I had come to Glasgow, not for any reason pertaining to Scotty, but to pick up Zoe and our new dog, Rufus, at my mom's house. She had generously dog sat for Kory and me while we spent our tenth anniversary in Paris.

I don't know what possessed me to make the fifteen-minute drive to the Lodge. I guess I figured while I was in town I might as well take it in. I had no reason to be there, no one to meet, and nothing in particular to view. I suppose I knew then that this would be the final time I would make the trip.

Kory stayed at the house with my mom and the dogs. He said he was allowing me some time alone with my thoughts. Personally, I knew he didn't care to visit the park, and had I not been so involved with Scotty's case, I wouldn't have either.

In the car I had been listening to "Behaviour," my favorite Pet Shop Boys album. "This Must Be The Place I've Waited Years To Leave" began playing on the stereo. I smiled. It was a favorite and had begun at just the right time.

Before I had even gotten to the town square I made a last minute decision and headed in the opposite direction. There was a place I had yet to visit and I felt it necessary to make the journey. Through Glasgow I drove along Edmonton Road, until I reached the town of Edmonton when the same route becomes Glasgow Road. That alone should explain a lot about my hometown.

Like Glasgow, Edmonton has been frozen in time. Empty storefronts, vacant sidewalks, and a plethora of fast food restaurants greet visitors. I drove on, headed through town, until I reached a small, country church and neighboring cemetery. I parked the car and got out. I had no clue as to where I was going, so I wandered.

Up and down rows of well-maintained gravestones I walked, noting how picturesque my surroundings were at that moment. It really was lovely, albeit somber. The trees were expansive and alive with small robins. The grounds were trimmed. Even the tombstones themselves appeared recently polished. Everything seemed fresh and renewed.

In what seemed like no time, I came across what I was searching. Carved in stone it read 'Jeremy Scott Martin, November 4, 1975 – June 10, 2004.' I stared at the name. Did anyone ever call him Jeremy, I wondered to myself. Or Scott? Like him, I too go by my middle name. I don't remember anyone ever calling me James, except telemarketers. I couldn't imagine him being a 'Jeremy.' It just didn't fit his personality. He was definitely a 'Scotty.'

I stood in front of the stone, looking around the countryside. How many times had Brandi been here, I imagined? Or his mother? In all these years she had never spoken to me about her son. I understood. I recalled what Brandi said of her during our first meeting. *"She doesn't feel like anything is necessary 'cause none of it's gonna bring him back. She believes that if anybody had anything to do with it, the Lord is gonna take care of that in the end."*

I felt like I should leave something for him before I took off. I don't visit cemeteries often and it seemed like the appropriate thing to do. In all the growth, there were no wild flowers around and I wasn't about to snag another gravestone's gestures. Talk about sacrilegious! So I strolled back to the car and rummaged around for a scrap of paper on which I scribbled a single word, placing it atop Scotty's name. *Faith.*

. . .

On the drive towards the state park I passed the same old, familiar scenes; the restaurants, the lake houses, the menacing billboards, although a newly constructed one appeared; or maybe one I hadn't noticed previously. *"If you were to die today where would you spend eternity?"* For me, these signs had lost their meaning. Their repetition was no longer effective. Like the trees behind them and the wooden fences in front of them, they merely faded into the scenery.

Upon entering the Park I slowed down to allow three horseback riders a chance to cross the road. They disappeared into the woods. I parked and walked down to the lakefront. It was the only location in which I found myself that day. I avoided the Lodge, stayed clear of the loading dock, and didn't bother going near the cabins. Instead I merely sat on a patch of bluegrass and stared out at the water. There were no guests in view.

My thoughts turned to the morning of May 30th, notably the misinformation that seemed to follow the investigation from the onset: the barge, the 30-foot wall, falling overboard.

Scotty's injuries were presumed to have been the result of an accident from the moment medics arrived. Once he had been flown to Vanderbilt all the reports indicated his fall was an accident. The notion of an alleged altercation was only brought up after Mark Nelson had told the park rangers what he heard during his morning visit to Cabin 507. The medical investigation report and the autopsy both stated his injuries as a result of an accident dated July 27, 2004 and August 26, 2004 respectively. KSP was still investigating the case at the time but the medical reports already deemed it an "accident." If the grand jury was presented with this information, it may have lead them to believe that there was no foul play.

Still so many answers I don't know/realize that to question is how we grow. "Proud" was stuck in my head. *So I step out of the ordinary/I can feel my soul ascending/I am on my way/Can't stop me now/And you can do the same.*

I had to face facts and come to the realization that no one was going to tell me what really happened the morning of May 30, 2004. Like police, Brandi, and a few others, I was now at a dead end. But at least I had made it this far. I felt like I knew more about this case than most and I was ready to share what I had learned along the way.

I sat there overlooking the water, barely moving. The trees were lush and tall and the leaves rested peacefully on their branches. The air was still and quiet. I felt tired, a bit depressed, and angry. I wasn't sure what to do; what my next move would be. I continued sitting on that patch of grass for the rest of the afternoon. Finally, I wandered back to the car. I drove out of the Park for the last time and headed home. Above me, the sky was perfectly clear.

ACKNOWLEDGMENTS

Sincere gratitude to all those interviewed.

Special thanks to Brandi Martin Duvall for sharing her life, her stories, and her willingness to assist at all costs. You have been a champion from the beginning and I find your generosity to be immeasurable. Your fortitude inspires me.

Much love to my mom who taught me lessons of honesty and integrity. Thank you for always supporting my decisions. And thank you for your strength, because little did you know, you gave that strength to me.

Thanks to my sister, the most creative person I know. If we weren't related, you'd still be one of my best friends.

Above all, to my husband, Kory, who has encouraged me and this project from the start. You have endured the exhaustive years of research and writing, never diminishing my attempts to accomplish the goals I set out to achieve. I can always count on you to be in my corner, fighting the good fight.

I hope I have made you all, including Scotty, proud.

ABOUT THE AUTHOR

One Town's Son is Kevin Troxall's first novel. He is a native of Glasgow, Kentucky and resides in Los Angeles.

To learn more, visit
www.onetownsson.com

CPSIA information can be obtained
at www.ICGtesting.com
Printed in the USA
LVOW13s1652070718
582799LV00012BA/914/P